REPRODUCTION IN MAN AND HIS ANCESTORS

FOR 700 MILLION YEARS

Richard Torpin M.D.

CONTENTS

FRONTISPIECE

"If all mankind minus one, were of one opinion, and only one person were of the contrary opinion, mankind would be no more justified in silencing that one person, than he, if he had the power, would be justified in silencing mankind. But the peculiar evil of silencing the expression of an opinion is, that it is robbing the human race; posterity as well as the existing generation; those who dissent from the opinion, still more than those who hold it. If the opinion is right, they are deprived of exchanging error for truth; if wrong, they lose what is almost as great a benefit, the clearer perception and livelier impression of truth, produced by its collision with error."

John Stuart Mill, Essay On Liberty, 1880

1

INTRODUCTION

This small volume is a condensation of a larger, documented, unpublished manuscript in respect to the embryological evolution of animals dating back some 700 million years. This work is based upon reports published in the literature in regard to the origins of the respective animals, each of which arose from a single celled egg, and upon what takes place to transform this cell into an embryo, the embryo into a fetus or larva and the final transformation into a tiny replica of one of its parents. Each individual repeats all of the previous stages back to the single celled egg. All individuals are required to pass through these stages, and the methods make a fascinating story. Thus, animals must be related to each other primarily through their embryology.

As it exists today, the biological world appears to be committed to the Linnaean classification of animals. This was developed by a score or more of biological students who were the successors of Linnaeus about 225 years ago. His only object was to name (family, genus and species in Latin) and thus catalog all known plants and animals. While most such students subscribe to Darwin's theory of evolution, produced a hundred years later, there is little application to the Linnaean classification so developed. Morphologically then animals, especially mammals, have been classified upon their ecologies. For instance, mammals that lived in trees or had such a background tended to look alike and to be classified together. In these tree-climbing mammals there evolved a superior visual sense; the eyes become large and tend to move to the front of the face for better bifocal vision. Thus, the primates were composed of the tree shrews, tarsiers, lemurs, monkeys, apes and mankind. This made a sort of progression. Since morphology is based upon long-time ecological pursuits, it should be quite obvious that a truer relationship must depend upon how the animals reproduce, especially in respect to the internal mechanisms of egg production and maturation into a tiny replica of one of the parents. Deviations in these processes are the means of creating families, genera and species. Had embryology arisen prior to the establishment of the Linnaean hypothesis, no doubt the modern viewpoint would be far different. Apparently the only abortive attempt on the part of embryology to take part in the determination of animal relationships was in Ernst Haeckel's dictim that each individual animal repeats the development of its group (ontogeny repeats phylogeny). This proved impractical in demonstrating relationships because up to hundreds of millions of years of evolution were condensed into a few weeks or months of gestation and many stages were slurred over or deleted.

For the past hundred years of embryology, investigations were directed to microscopic details of various eutherian mammalian placentas. The gross aspects and intrauterine relationships were not emphasized, and authorities have come to agree that the placenta itself can be of little phylogenetic significance.

Certainly all mammals with a simplex uterus must be closely related and thus set apart from those with a bicornuate uterus, where the gestation sacs are located along the lumen of one of the two uterine horns.

The originality of Linnaeus was limited to two features. He removed whales and dolphins from the realm of fishes and correctly placed them among the eutherian mammals. Likewise, he removed the bats from the realm of birds and placed them among the eutherian mammals. In fact, he is said to have placed them tentatively with the primates.

After the Linnaean classification was well established and about 100 years following the final publication of his *Systema Naturae* in 1758, Darwin proposed the theory of evolution and this, almost universally, was accepted by biologists. However, in the 125 years since then there never has arisen any direct application to the Linnaean classification.

This present thesis reviews the embryology of animals beginning with the single celled protozoa, through the invertebrates and the vertebrates which made use of the simple yolked egg in reproduction, and through the vertebrates on land which employed the simple yolked egg housed within its blastocyst capsule. This capsule container not only implanted in relation to the maternal reproductive tract, but it also became the means of oxygenation, hydration and nutrition to the enclosed embryo which later became the fetus. The fetus remains in the blastocyst until birth.

Any classification of animals based upon continuing

4

embryology embodies, at every point, the Darwinian theory of evolution. Families, genera and species were related through their embryology, but their form and shape were dependent upon millions of years of ecological pursuits. Thus groups could have almost identical embryology with great divergence of morphology. It is embryology which determines their true relationships.

THE ORIGIN OF LIFE AND EARLY METAZOAN ANIMALS

In a recent essay on Precambrian life, Nitecki, 1973, described three fossil windows opening back into this unimaginable expanse of time. This was based upon the work of Barghoorn, Tyler, Schopf and associates, beginning about 1950. The oldest known microscopic fossil organisms appeared in black cherty rocks 3 billion years old and were found in the Fig Tree Formation of South Africa. Chert, formed around still living cells as a gel covering, preserved the morphological structures as they became impregnated with a variety of silicon often found in the sea bottom. Actual cell division has been noted. These early cells were protoplasm without nuclei (prokaryote) but they possessed extraordinary ability to utilize sunlight to synthesize carbohydrates and proteins directly from the abundant supply of minerals of the earth's surface and collected in the seas. They increased in size until their mass outran the necessary surface area and then they reproduced by fission. Some of their modern descendants are the blue-green algae.

These were extremely versatile, some were aerobic and some anaerobic. They could adapt to various light frequencies, to heat and cold and to all sorts of ecologies. Some had ability to move. They were primitive only in the lack of cell organelles and their origin must have been far earlier than 3 billion years ago.

5

The second window into this far distant world was known as the Gunflint Formation in Canada and Michigan, approximately 2 billion years old, and this contains iron ore. Recently well documented precambrian organisms were found in it. While there is evidence of breakdown of chlorophyl the cells still were prokaryote (without nuclei). Sometimes the gel surrounding the living organism had the ability to incorporate finely laminated sedimentary, calcareous structures, mostly found in blue-green algae. These piled-up structures were known as stromabolites. In the precambrian deposits they owe their luxuriant growth to lack of grazing snails.

The third window into the Precambrian era is the Bitter Springs Formation of central Australia, about 1 billion years old. These fossils also were produced in chert. This is the first general appearance of nucleated cells (eukaryote) which must have originated sometime previously. The nucleus contains the chromosomes which house the genes. For the first time sex was possible because cell division originates in the nucleus and each half contains half of the chromosomes and half of the paired genes. Thus in the reconstruction of the cell one half of a cell could join with one half from another, thus introducing similar, new but slightly different genes. This was the foundation of sex about a billion years ago. Sex was employed in all subsequent plant and animal life and was the basis for the creation of orders, families, genera and species. These were based upon constant genetic probing and the survival of the fittest.

A more recent fossil window, just prior to the onset of the Cambrian era, six hundred million years ago, was in South Australia and is known as the Ediacara Fauna. These were the oldest known animals and were soft-skinned. Their exact body imprints were preserved in mud which hardened into rock. While these were the earliest so far found, they were well advanced at tissue organ level of development and had muscular, digestive, reproductive and respiratory organs.

Evolution, as it is understood, may not be upwards but more or less sidewise. Apparently animals evolved from the main stem of plant life some 6 or 7 hundred million years ago. Each animal cell received every feature of the plant cell except one. This was retained by the plant cell and consisted of the ability to synthesize nutrition directly from chemical constituents. Thus, although the animal cells had the important property of sexual evolution, they were forever dependent upon plant life for nutrition. This was a symbiotic union that so far has not been broken. It was of advantage to both parties. It kept the oceans from becoming filled and clogged with plant life. Animals, especially birds, could aid in the dissemination of plant life. It gave the animals ready processed carbohydrates and proteins. The gaseous waste product of plants, oxygen, was employed by animals in exchange for a gaseous waste product, carbon dioxide. One might consider that all animals are carnivorous, eating once living cells of plants or of other animals who had eaten cells of plants. When the animal processed the food the waste became fertilizer for plants, and when animals died their disintegrated bodies were so used by plants.

This was a perfect symbiosis and probably the chief reason for its success. Since civilization began a very relatively short time ago man's principal occupation has been with agriculture either for food for himself or for his captive and tamed grazing animals which he used for food. The results truly have been prodigious.

It may be stated that the non-nucleated cell (prokaryote) was created more than 3 billion years ago and that it required about 2 billion years to add the nu-

7

cleus and associated sex to the living cell. Thus all subsequent plants and all animals are eukaryote, and generally reproduce by union of male and female sex cells.

The earth has been dated to be about four and one half billion years old. By now there are three great groups of matter, mineral, vegetable and animal. Minerals were present since the earth began. There is evidence that about 3 billion years ago minerals in the warm salt water seas, aided by energy from sunlight and possibly lightning from electrical storms, somehow became associated to form simple amino-acids. These in turn became associated to form proteins. Thus a single living cell arose, and when this tiny blob of protein increased in size, its volume outran its necessary surface area and it then divided into two cells. This process continued as long as minerals and sunlight held out, ad infinitum.

There is evidence also that it required 2 billion years to evolve a nucleus for the cell. The nucleus then became the controller of metabolism and the bearer of the genes, split equally to each daughter cell for inheritance.. This nucleated cell was originated about one billion (1000 million) years ago and continued to synthesize its own amino-acids and proteins. It used carbon and water to synthesize carbohydrates from minerals, energized by sunlight, for another 300 million years before a very significant occurrence began, originated from heretofore solely plant life. A new nucleated cell was evolved which had all living attributes of the vegetable cell except one. It was not granted the ability to synthesize its own essential amino-acids but had to acquire these by consuming plant life. These new cells became the origin of the animal kingdom and by consuming plants aided in prevention of uncontrolled plant growth. These single celled animals, (protozoa), of which there are stated to be 50,000 varieties, at first were very individualistic and lived and reproduced by themselves. However, some became associated in groups to form sponges, etc. Finally this tendency to association produced multiple celled animals, metazoa. Although in some instances these animals could separate into two parts, each of which could become a new animal, in general, all metazoa designated special cells, ova, to carry out sexual reproduction.

The vertebrates are bilaterally symmetrical, longitudinally orientated animals with a stiff, central cartilaginous rod and upon this rod much later was built the vertebral column. The cells designated to carry out reproduction, the eggs, were formed in the female ovaries which originated from ridges in the wall of the internal (coelomic) body cavity. The ovarian follicles (housing for developing eggs) were near the surface of the two ovaries. When the protoplasm was fully formed and was bound to a quantity of yolk (food for the embryo) these two combined items were expelled from the ruptured follicles into the body cavity. Likewise the sperms were formed in bilateral male gonads, the testes. In the early vertebrates the eggs and sperms escaped into the surrounding water through primitive uriniferous tubules leading from the central coelomic cavity to the outside of the body where fertilization occurred in water. To insure this there were elaborated sex hormones (very similar in all animals) to attract the attention of the males at the correct time.

Lets consider the early vertebrates which originated in salt sea water some five or six hundred million years ago. Unlike the more primitive invertebrates these were longitudinal in shape and possessed a longitudinally placed cartilaginous rod probably for stiffening. Around this rod they, much later, evolved the vertebral column. Since these were very primitive vertebrates they had the following features. Their body fluids were identical in salt content of sodium, potassium, magnesium, calcium and phosphorus as was possessed by the outside sea water. Thus their skin was very thin and porous. Sea water easily entered and mixed with the body plasma which was principally sea water. They also possessed a muscularized tail for propulsion, but no skeleton. They had no fins and the mouth was round and sucker-like. They probably were bottom feeders consuming vegetation and small invertebrates. They had primitive eyes and a good sense of smell. They had a simple excretory system of lateral ducts extending from the coelomic cavity which was drained to the outside water. These ducts served for exit of the eggs and sperms created in gonads arising from folds in the lining of the coelomic cavity.

Now it so happens that a new supply of minerals was constantly being washed down from the coastal mountains by rains and floods. Thus the food supply was improved along the fresh water coastal regions. Plant life and invertebrates had already made the transition to these fresh waters, and the vertebrates attempted to follow suit. However, when they got into brackish waters, fresh water flowed in through their thin skin to dilute the sea water salt content of their body fluids. They had to retreat to the sea and proceeded to evolve a fresh water proof skin to protect their body fluids from dilution. After slow evolution, by the time that they returned to the fresh waters along the coast, they were equipped with almost submarine-like casing — a tough, hard keratinous waterproof sheath. On certain areas this rigid covering produced spines, some of which became movable and equipped with muscles. These developed principally in two lateral regions, the shoulder to become pectoral fins and in the anal region to become pelvic fins. In further evolution fins became arms or legs or, in the case of birds and bats, supports for wings. The head end of this rigid casing, was evolved into the muscularized, hinged and predatory jaw, often supplied with modified skin teeth. These weird appearing animals in fresh water became the basic ostracoderms (Gr. shellskinned). They then became the basis for all future vertebrate evolution, including those that went back to the salt water seas and those that chose to come out on land and live in air. All sea living vertebrates, which have fins and rigid jaws (sharks and marine fishes) and all vertebrates living and reproducing on land (reptiles, birds, monotremes, marsupials and eutherian mammals) arose as descendants of the fresh water ostracoderms.

Since their skin was tough and oxygen could no longer perfuse inward, they evolved gills for oxygenation. These were long vascularized filaments extending into the water to allow oxygen to perfuse directly into the blood stream, which by now had become a closed circulation system developed in fresh water. They also improved upon the internal excretory system to protect against loss of vital sea-water-acquired body fluids. This was first achieved by segmentally located tubules leading from the central coelomic body cavity. When the closed blood circulation appeared, end-artery tufts of capillaries appropriated the coelomic inner ends of these tubules. These already had become selective in permitting waste products to escape while recovering essential elements of the blood filtrate.

These ostracoderms also began to develop an internal bony skeleton whereby the outside tough and rigid skin casing could soften into pliable yet watertight skin.

The ostracoderms gave rise to four great groups of animal descendants, all equipped with fins, or arms and legs, and a hinged predatory jaw. These four groups were (1) lungfish, (2) sharks, (3) marine fishes and (4) amphibians.

While fresh water in which these animals first lived

had plenty of food, it soon became apparent that these fresh waters also had defects. Due to stagnation, drought and decaying vegetation, oxygen dissolved in the water periodically became deficient. Consequently these four immediate descendants of the ostracoderms had the urge to depart from the fresh water. Only one group among the four groups remained in fresh water, which was subject to oxygen depletion. The stubborn lungfish did not leave but set about to develop a carburetor to secure oxygen from air. Thus it developed the lung, which after all is simply an inverted gill system with the highly vascularized filaments inverted and placed internally within the chest region. Since the embryonic lung bud developed from the anterior surface of the oesophagus, it may be assumed that it first may have accommodated oxygenated water. The lungfish then every ten minutes or so rises to the surface of the more or less stagnated water and takes in a lung full of highly oxygenated air. During their lifetime in water, eggs are deposited and externally fertilized. The embryos mature in water for the next generation. When the inevitable drought comes, the lungfish is able to burrow into the mud, double itself up and create an impervious slime casing surrounded by mud with a small hole leading from its mouth to the surface. All metabolic processes slow to mere existence, possibly for several years, until the floods return, softening the mud and releasing the fish from its dried mud casing. Such places exist today in certain areas on the earth's surface (Africa, South America and Australia). Some of the young lungfishes are equipped with gills prior to the developing of lungs. Thus the lungfish has succeeded in surviving through several hundred million years, a relic of a very successful invention, the lung. Homer Smith, 1961, presented a first-hand account of the lungfish.

The other three immediate descendant groups from the shell-skinned ostracoderms all left these oxygen depleted fresh waters. The sharks and marine fishes went back to the well-oxygenated salt water seas. The amphibians, equipped with legs in place of fins, and, in our own direct line, succeeded in coming out onto land to live in and breathe air, but they had some problems which will be related later in this account.

First, let us go back to see what happened to those metazoan animals more primitive than the vertebrates already considered. Since these earlier animals had no notochord for longitudinal stiffening from which to construct the vertebral column, they are called invertebrates. Their bodies generally were rounded and compact often with radiating parts and not longitudinal in shape except the worms, which were bilaterally symmetrical, a feature later adopted by the vertebrates.

All of these were metazoan (multiple celled animals) and originated in the salt water seas where they obtained a sea water body fluid content. Now these also migrated to fresh water coastal regions where their plant food supply had already preceded them. Just as did the later vertebrates these invertebrates evolved a tough, waterproof keratinous covering to hold out fresh water from diluting their sea water obtained body fluid content. Likewise, to retain salts they evolved a primitive selective excretory system. Spines on the exoskeleton became internally supplied with muscles to originate fins or arms or legs. The head end of the keratinized skin became a hinged jaw to replace the former, soft, round (cyclostome) mouth. Reproduction was by single celled eggs with the yolk, expelled by the female and fertilized usually externally in water by male sperms spread over them.

How did they obtain oxygen? The new and tough waterproof skin likewise resisted inward perfusion of oxygen in water. Thus they evolved multiple canals (called tracheae) leading into their bodies from the outside rigid covering. This was important because when they came from water to land, air entered these tracheae and gave off oxygen to the fluids filling the inner ends of the canals. Now when they emerged from water to air on land, respiration was no problem, but reproduction required some modifications. The eggs in water were perfectly moist and viable but on land they became desiccated. However, this was obviated by the female reproductive tract applying a waterproof keratinous covering to the eggs before expulsion. Consequently the eggs had to be fertilized prior to this by internal fertilization, of which two methods were developed. (1) the sperms could be expelled from the male in packets called spermatophores and these later picked up by the female cloaca, (2) by male-female copulation prior to application of the egg coating. This second method became quite generalized among the invertebrates living in air on land. A modification of this is that some invertebrate females, as also in some vertebrate fish females, are able to store one batch of viable sperms for several successive gestations. In some arthropods, especially spiders, there is pugnacious disposition in the individuals and females may kill and eat the males. Here the usual method of internal fertilization is by spermatophores.

This account shows that all metazoan animals living in air on land received their sea-water body fluids from the sea but that in order to protect these body fluids, they must have had a sojourn first in fresh water before making the migration to air on land. However, many invertebrates, indigenous to the sea, inhabit the sea but if they have a waterproof casing, fins, arms or legs and a hinged predatory mouth, they must have received these not in sea water but from a time spent in fresh water.

The chief feature of the invertebrates was that they were satisfied with the exoskeleton and never bothered to create a mesodermic, internal, rigid cartilaginous or

14

calcified skeleton. This had some advantages. The rigid exoskeleton gave firm foundation for arms, legs and jaws. It was light in weight, which may account for myriads of invertebrates that evolved wings for flight in air as they became land dwellers.

SUMMARY

Rains and rivers eroded the land masses and carried chemicals into the fresh water coastal regions. Plant life, evolved in the salt water sea, migrated to the coastal regions for fresh supplies of minerals. Invertebrates, whose food was plant life, followed. The vertebrates evolved in the sea, and when their plant and invertebrate food came to the coastal regions, the vertebrates did likewise. Both invertebrates and vertebrates were required to protect their seawater-acquired body fluids, and both developed selective excretory systems and rigid waterproof skins from which both fabricated fins, arms or legs and a predatory jaw.

This exoskeleton remained satisfactory to the invertebrates, in water or on land, but the vertebrates created an internal cartilaginous or calcareous skeleton and then allowed the hard casing, exoskeleton to soften into still, waterproof skin.

SYNOPSIS OF EVOLUTION AND REPRODUCTION

There is evidence that the non-nucleated (prokaryote) cells were present on earth at least 3 billion years ago. It required approximately 2 billion years to add the nuclei and associated heterosexual features. The nucleated eukaryote (sex potential) single cell of living protoplasm then required possibly several hundred million years to become metazoan with multiple cells and specialization. This was present in the Ediacara Fauna about 600 million years ago, which no doubt possessed an anamniote egg in these invertebrates. The anamniote egg then was the mode of reproduction, oviparity to ovoviviparity on to true viviparity in water or on land until the amphibians developed the remarkable blastocyst 350 million years ago. From then through blastocyst oviparity, ovoviviparity and true viviparity was another 150 Myears. Viviparity in marsupials first employed yolk-sac fetal vascularization of the trophoblastic surface of the blastocyst but about 200 million years ago the allantois began to take over from the yolk-sac in this respect and at about 60 or 70 million years ago the great and subsequently dominant allanto-placental eutherian mammalian line began. At first the blastocyst lay free in a segment of the lumen of one tube of a bicornuate uterus. Very rapidly, in a space of possibly ten million years the whole eutherian mammalian line was created. This involved a journey of the blastocyst from the uterine lumen to progressive invasion of the uterine mucosal wall until it was able to bury itself within the mucosa of a horn of a bicornuate uterus, in the vampire bat. Further evolution had resulted in the reduction of the number of simultaneous gestations to one or two and the assimilation of the shortening horns into one simplex body. This occurred only in the bats which in turn produced the first simplex uterus and these mammals, only, presented it to all primates of which phyllostomid bats, African giant water shrews, armadillos, South American sloths and anteaters must be included.

EGG DEVELOPMENT AND EGG SIZE

Every egg essentially is the living protoplasm destined to form the embryo. This is created by the ovary which also adds varying amounts of food in the form of the yolk. The protoplasm and yolk are bound together by a circumscribing membrane with which they leave the ovary. If the egg is to be expelled from the mother's reproductive tract to be incubated and hatched outside, then it requires a great deal of added protection and often added food. These are produced in the maternal reproductive tract in the form of egg-white albumen, mainly water, and a keratinous or calcareous shell to retain water but which is pervious to oxygen and carbon dioxide.

Carl Hartman, 1929, compiled a fascinating and well documented paper on the size of the egg. This work was devoted primarily to the amniote mammalian egg. Marshall's *Physiology of Reproduction* volume 2, page 10 cites the classical literature upon the anamniote eggs of fishes, etc.

In general, it may be stated that all ovaries of all animals provide some yolk to every egg, either to start the embryonic development or to carry the nourishment throughout its embryonic life. It so happens that in the latter group of animals where the embryo depends more or less exclusively upon the yolk deposit, this situation has occurred in only two dissimilar groups. The first of these was in very primitive sharks and their relatives, dogfish, rays, skates, etc. In this group, in the oviparous forms there is prolonged incubation and the embryo presumably had not yet acquired the ability to obtain extraneous food by swallowing, such as seems to have been possessed by all later fishes. Thus the yolk deposit in shark eggs was enough to complete embryonic development. In subsequent fishes the embryo precociously swallowed sea water with food in oviparous forms, or uterine gland secretions in viviparous forms. This reached its climax in the amphibian urodele *Salamandra atra* in which upwards of 60 embryos are reduced in number to one to four by cannibalism within the uterus. Such was possible because the embryo lay on top of its yolk sac and was free of covering membranes (anamniote). Thus, the amount of yolk in all calcareous bony fishes could be and was reduced. This reduction became still more pronounced in viviparous amniote, blastocystic vertebrates, the principal groups of which were marsupial and eutherian mammals. In these, this was accomplished by the development of a placenta in the covering membrane (trophoblast) of the blastocyst. This device augmented the nutrition received from the mother's reproductive tract and reduced dependence upon the yolk deposited by the ovary.

All mammalian eggs, with the exception of egg-laying monotremes are extremely small, measuring in the neighborhood of 100 micra in diameter in eutheria. The eggs of marsupials, in general, are not much more than twice the diameter of eutherian mammals. Other than sharks, viviparous (anamniote) fishes and amphibians have relatively small eggs due to the reduced amount of yolk deposited in them. This is possible because of the precocious nature of the embryos in early swallowing of uterine gland secretions with lessened dependence upon yolk for nutrition. The same holds for oviparous, anamniote types which were able to swallow surrounding food-laden water.

In amniote (blastocystic) animals, reptiles, birds, monotremes, marsupials and eutherian mammals, the size of the egg (amount of yolk deposited) depends upon whether the animal is oviparous or viviparous. In all instances the embryo is imprisoned within its amniotic cavity and the only source of nutrition must come either from its blastocyst enclosed yolk deposit in oviparous forms or from its fetal-vascularized trophoblast absorption from its neighborhood uterine gland secretions, or trophoblastic (placental) attachment to the uterine wall in the viviparous varieties. In the oviparous amniote varieties, reptiles, birds, and monotremes, the egg necessarily is comparatively enormous due to the large amount of yolk and all encased in a protective keratinous or calcareous outer shell. These eggs vary in size from a centimeter or so in greatest diameter in monotremes and hummingbirds, to 13x

15.5 cm in ostriches and on up to the very large eggs of extinct dinosaurs. Boyd and Hamilton, 1958, in Marshall's *Physiology of Reproduction* state that the now extinct *Aepyornis* had a shell measuring 37.5 by 24 cm and a cubic content of approximately two gallons.

Romer, 1957, illustrated the oldest known amniote egg from sediment laid down in the lower Permian period in Texas. According to the geological table in LeGros Clark's *History of the Primates*, the age of this specimen should be more than 200 million years.

Let it be reiterated that in all of the animal kingdom there are only two situations in which the egg is of relatively enormous size due to the large quantities of yolk. The first of these occurred in primitive anamniote elasmobranchs, the sharks, rays and skates, dogfish etc. This must be due to the inability of the embyro in these specific instances to acquire extraneous nutrition and thus must depend entirely upon a sufficient yolk supply. The other large-yolk situation occurs in oviparous amniotes; dinosaurs, reptiles and birds and monotremes. In these with a shell-covering, the homologue of the blastocyst's trophoblast, the sole nutrition of the embryo must come from the yolk and added egg white. In monotremes the egg is relatively small since the embryos are born immature.

This, I believe, answers the question 'Why may sharks eggs be millions of times larger than whale eggs?' According to geological time scales sharks may have upwards of 500 million years of life history while whales (eutherian mammals) may have not more than 60 or 70 million. The shark may be several times as old as the whale in ancestors but tremendous inventions of reproduction occurred in the interval.

In the primitive eggs of the metazoans (multiple celled animals) some 600 million years ago the maternal ovary-created yolk was the principal source of

19

nutrition for the embryo until it could obtain food by mouth from the environment. This was the situation in all invertebrates and in the pre-amphibian vertebrates, sharks and fishes; in the amphibians and in the egg-laying reptiles, birds and monotremes. The former had simple yolked eggs but the reptiles, birds and monotremes had blastocysts which were created by the embryonic living protoplasm between the time of fertilization and the beginning of maturation (implantation).

In all of these animals the yolk remained as an integral globule (meroblastic cleavage) and the entodermic midgut of the embryo extended around it. In all viviparous mammals, marsupial and eutherian, the amount of yolk produced by the maternal ovary was greatly reduced, more so in the eutherian mammals than in the marsupials. However, in both groups the cleavage of the egg was holoblastic so that each new cell received its share of yolk and there was none to be surrounded by the yolk-sac. This did not prevent the yolk-sac from forming as an outpouching of the midgut tube.

In viviparous mammals the yolk-sac assumed an entirely new role. i.e. to take part, if possible, in vascularization of the trophoblast covering of the blastocyst. The trophoblast presented itself to the uterine tissues, or secretions, and prior to development of the fetal circulation it was the sole and primary placenta. The secondary placenta became trophoblast, vascularized by yolk-sac fetal vessels and in the eutherian mammals the tertiary placenta was trophoblast vascularized by allantoic fetal vessels. In some early eutherian mammals, subungulates and browsing artiodactyla and in the late simplex uterine primates the yolk-sac placenta never formed because the yolk-sac did not enlarge to touch and vascularize the trophoblast. Thus these eutherian mammals had only two of the three theoretical, consecutive placentas, primary trophoblast and tertiary, allantoic vascularized trophoblast, However, in all instances in eutherian mammals the first two placentas were only temporary and by midgestation had been superseded by the definitive allantoic vascularized placenta.

The marsupials, in general, had only the first two placentas; non-vascularized trophoblast and yolk-sac vascularized trophoblast and no allantoic placenta occurred except in the bandicoots (Perameles). Here it appeared to be accessory and of no consequence in altering the early expulsion of the fetus.

It should be obvious that when the embryo develops independently outside of the mother's body and the newly hatched must be able to shift for itself, then the amount of yolk must be voluminous. This is the situation in oviparous sharks, egg laying reptiles, including dinosaurs, and in birds.

EVOLUTION OF OVARIES AND TESTES

In the primitive vertebrates, originated in sea water possibly 600 million years ago, when the three germ layers folded ventralward to form the longitudinal body, there was a closed cavity, coelomic, lying outside of the entodermic gut tube and inside of the mesodermic frame work. Bilateral ridges appeared in the wall of this cavity to develop into the gonads, the ovaries or testes. See figure 1 (one). The eggs and the sperms escaped into the closed coelomic cavity. The only exits were segmentally placed uriniferous tubules draining this cavity to the outside water. Eggs and sperms escaped through these tubules.

Thus the early sea water vertebrates had from the beginning the following organs (1) a very thin skin through which oxygenated sea water readily perfused, (2) a sea water body fluid, (3) the beginnings of sense organs, smell, sensitivity to light and temperature,

21

developed in the skin covering, (4) an entodermic gut tube supplied with a cylostome mouth for nutrition, (5) bilateral segmental uriniferous tubules to drain the coelomic cavity and to provide exit for eggs and sperms produced in the ovaries or testes. Locomotion was provided by a movable tail. There was no circulatory system except by body contraction and osmosis in a primitive lymphatic system.

When these primitive vertebrates migrated to fresh water, they first of all were required to develop an ectodermic skin capable of holding out fresh water from diluting their sea water acquired body fluids. Thus they keratinized their covering into a virtual water proof rigid casing. Spines appearing on this casing were mobilized into pectoral and pelvic fins. From the head end of this rigid skin they developed a hinged and predatory jaw later equipped with teeth and all originated from skin. In fresh water they also acquired a blood circulatory system which began with a muscular pump to cause movement of the body fluids. This emerged into an open circulation where the body fluids were merely pumped from the head end to the tail end of the body. Here, in fresh water there evolved a closed blood circulation with arteries and veins connected by capillaries. When this happened certain end arterial capillary tufts appropriated the coelomic ends of the uriniferous tubules to create glomeruli and eventually kidneys for urinary excretion. This expropriation left the eggs and sperms with no exit from the coelomic cavity. In the male an accommodation with the urinary tract was made and sperms escaped through the terminal urinary duct. The ovaries on the other hand could not form such an accommodation and thus a new pair of ridges arose in the wall of the coelomic cavity. These gave rise to a new set of tubes draining the coelomic cavity to be used exclusively by the eggs of the female. This new Muellerian duct system created the Fallopian tubes, the two horns of the uterus (eventually fused into one in the later evolved eutherian mammals) and the upper portion of the vagina leading to the cloaca or urogenital sinus but ultimately to become an independent exit.

Primarily these Muellerian ducts served only for passage of the eggs. Later the eggs remained in the uterus to be hatched and born alive. Still later the eggs, devoid of shell, developed embryos supplied with extraembryonic membranes that could secure nutrition from the secretions of the uterine mucosa. Still later the extraembryonic membranes produced placentas, at first entirely fetal in composition, but later able to attach to the uterine wall and in the final evolution (primates including the human female) the blastocyst was able to erode a cavity in the uterine mucosal wall for complete burial of the blastocyst by which time varying degrees of villous hemochorial placentation had evolved.

During this long period of time, the ovaries remained in the abdominal coelomic cavity but the testes had a tendency to migrate outside of this cavity to a scrotal sac below the perineum. The probable reason was to secure a more optimal environmental temperature for the development of sperms.

The most primitive animal required two features; how to obtain food and how to reproduce. Thus the mouth and intestine and the ovaries and testes were among the first organs to evolve simultaneously along with organs of excretion of metabolic wastes.

FROM EGG TO EMBRYO

The egg is composed of a minute quantity of living protoplasm bound by a membrane to a variable quantity of yolk (food for the emerging embryo). Both living protoplasm and yolk are produced by the maternal ovary. The human egg was discovered by von

Baer in 1827. The complex method by which the single-celled mammalian egg evolves into an embryo required several decades to elucidate. While this process may be devious in specific cases, substantially it may be briefly described as follows.

As in the protozoa, the egg enlarges and divides into two cells. When the amount of yolk in the metazoan egg is small as in most viviparous vertebrates, the cell division includes the yolk also, holoblastic, but when the yolk appears in a large quantity as in oviparous and viviparous sharks, some fishes, reptiles, birds, monotremes and in some ovoviviparous vertebrates the amount of yolk deposited by the maternal ovary is large. In these situations the living protoplasm is the only part that divides in cell division, meroblastic.

The succeeding cells all divide, as the first, but remain together to form sheets of cellular membrane. Eventually there appear three such superimposed sheets, ectoderm, mesoderm and entoderm. These might be visualized as a pile of three pancakes. Now if these three pancakes are lifted up as a unit and folded ventralward, the top pancake would form the outside surface of an elongated body, with the bottom pancake forming a central tube from end to end. In the model the top pancake forms the ectodermic covering and originates the sensory system. The middle pancake represents the mesoderm with the bony skeleton and circulatory system and the bottom pancake simulates the entodermic gut canal. Thus the embryo is formed but it must be connected to its food supply previously stored in the yolk. This is accomplished by entoderm from the ventral region of the midgut elaborating an entodermic cell membrane to surround and enclose the volume of yolk. Thus, when the fetal circulation develops, the yolk-sac surrounding the yolk becomes fetally vascularized, and the entodermic yolk-sac cells digest the yolk and these products enter the fetal blood stream. Oxygen from the environment could perfuse into the exposed fetal yolk-sac vessels but this is only incidental to the function of the yolk-sac, which primarily is nutritional.

By oxygen perfusion inward, the extensive surface ectodermic area of the embryo becomes the chief source of oxygenation. When the yolk is exhausted the embryo then must secure nutrition by mouth from the watery environment.

Such is the mechanism of development of all embryos. For the first half of the nearly 700 million years of animal life on earth it remained as described, and in almost all instances the embryo was naked, attached to its yolk-sac, in a watery environment. These were known as anamniote. Reproduction occurred by female deposition of the eggs in water where fertilization was accomplished by male sperms spread over them. In some instances viviparity evolved where the eggs, necessarily internally fertilized, still matured in a watery environment created by maternal secretions into the retaining reproductive channel.

Invertebrates evolved in the sea and many came to fresh water where they developed a tough, water impervious skin (exoskeleton) to hold out fresh water from diluting their sea-water acquired body fluid content of salts. They also evolved primitive kidney systems to maintain their body fluids intact. Probably due to oxygen depletion in fresh water some emerged from fresh water to live in air on land. Here the anamniote eggs (yolk and potential embryo) soon dried out in air. This was counteracted by the maternal reproductive tract in secreting around the egg a water-proof keratinous shell, but even here the embryo first developed in a retained pool of water. Emergence on land required a drastic change in egg fertilization. No longer could the female deposited eggs be fertilized by spreading sperms over them

A

1.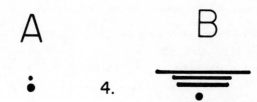

2.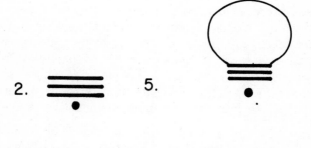

3.

B

4.

5.

6.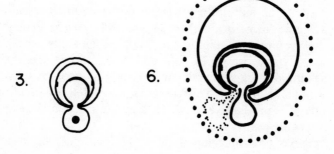

Fig. 1.—Development of the embryo from a single celled egg. A, 1, represents the tiny living protoplasm bound to its larger yolk. In A, 2, the single cell divides and eventually forms the three germ layers above the yolk and these fold ventralward to create the embryo with its top layer forming the skin covering (ectolerm), the middle layer, the framework, bones, muscles and blood vessels (mesoderm) and the bottom layer, the gut tube (entoderm). This latter alimentary tube is surrounded by the coelomic body cavity, from ridges (depicted) in the inner wall of which are formed the bilateral gonads for reproduction. The gut protrudes its wall ventrally to form the yolk-sac which surrounds the yolk for nutrition to the embryo. Oxygen perfuses into the embryo through its skin or gills.

This system was used by all multiple celled animals (metazoa) for 350 million years (the first half of 700 million years of animal life on earth) and still is employed by their direct descendants. They included all invertebrates and all of the primitive vertebrates, sharks, fishes and amphibians with the exception of the highly advanced amphibian which created the blastocyst shown in B, 4, 5, 6. This latter was a housing for the embryo of all such amphibian descendants, reptiles, birds, monotremes, marsupials and eutherian mammals. The embryo was no longer free and independent in its environment but was imprisoned in its housing blastocyst whose wall took care of all of its needs.

B, 4, represents the embryonic stage of A, 2, but here the top germ layer first folds dorsalward to form the amniotic cavity in which the future embryo-fetus resides surrounded by water. When this is completed the three germ layers then fold ventralward pushing the embryo up into its amniotic cavity. The embryo is identical to that in A, 3, but it is protected in the amniotic cavity in the blastocyst. The yolk-sac forms to surround the yolk. However, in marsupials and in eutherian mammals there is no yolk to surround because it had been divided equally to each daughter cell. The yolk-sac forms as formerly but in these placental mammals it takes part in fetal vascularizing the chorionic trophoblast shown in the outside dotted line. This is the extraembryonic tissue that presents to the uterine mucosal lining. The yolk-sac thus can, as always before, take care of supplying nutrition to the imprisoned embryo. But its ability to acquire oxygen was deficient. Consequently a new gut sac was developed, the allantois, originally to store waste fetal products but which became the acquisitor of oxygen from the environment. It expanded and spread to underlie the trophoblast which its vessels vascularized.

In this process in the eutherian mammals it detaches and eliminates any previous involvement of the yolk-sac in the formation of the placenta. On the other hand the marsupials employ the yolk-sac placenta and only one group (Perameles) adds a rather inefficient allantoic portion.

(external fertilization) but internal fertilization became necessary, either by packets of sperms (spermatophores) later picked up by the female cloaca or, more commonly used, by male-female copulation prior to the deposition of the keratinous covering. On the other hand the oviparous sharks, which remained in water, also had an expansible keratinous covering to the anamniote egg. This covering was pervious not only to oxygen but to water and probably to some food elements.

Try as they did, the amphibians never were able to convert the anamniote egg to use in air on land. But the persistent experimentation resulted in folding the extraembryonic extension of the ectoderm dorsalward to create the subsequently water filled amniote cavity. Now when the three germ layers were folded ventralward, the embryo found itself in a watery environment in the amniote cavity and the yolk-sac lay outside of this cavity. The amphibians surrounded the amniote sac and the outlying yolk-sac by a covering membrane, the trophoblast, to create the closed blastocyst. Now there was found to be no exit for fetal waste products and a second ventral gut-sac, the allantois, from near the rectum was evolved to store waste products. Fortunately this allantoic sac assumed the oxygen-securing property by spreading and underlying the trophoblast covering of the blastocyst. The fetal circulation then could develop vascularization of two entodermic sacs, the yolk-sac for nutrition and the allantoic sac for oxygenation.

During much of the first 100 million years of management of the blastocyst by the reptiles (likewise in birds) the blastocyst, with a great quantity of yolk and an oxygen-pervious shell, was deposited outside of the maternal body for incubation. It is obvious that the only control of the amount of the amniotic fluid devolved upon the embyo-fetus. It is very unlikely that this highly efficient system was ever modified when the blastocyst was retained in the maternal reproductive tract as in all viviparous mammals. Thus the primitive independence of the embryo-fetus was maintained to a degree in the intrauterine development in mammals.

In the early stages of intrauterine gestation the very thin skin of the embryo probably allows dispersion of fluid from the embryo to the amniote sac. After the fetus is formed and the organs are developed there appear to be two avenues of fluid escape from the embryo-fetus, the sweat glands and the urinary tract. There also appear to be two avenues of fluid escape from the amniote cavity, through the fetal gastrointestinal tract and through the fetal lungs. As in the shell-covered eggs matured outside of the maternal body, the amnio-chorionic covering of the blastocyst appears to be relatively waterproof.

Fortunately for our knowledge each of the representative stages in the embryological evolution appears to have been satisfactory to certain species of animals and these continued to employ the same method, then received, throughout the hundreds of millions of years to the present time. Fortunately paleontological evidence may be used to determine the time origin of these animals so well documented in their embryology.

In the final years of the past century Ernst Haeckel, 1899, produced his famous dictum that ontogeny (development of each individual animal) repeats phylogeny (development of the families, genera and species). This applies so accurately to the human embryo which in nine months has successive stages that correspond to each of the major events in the hundreds of million years of evolution of the vertebrates. One of the great contributions of Streeter when he was research associate in the department of embryology at the Carnegie Institution of Washington, Baltimore, was his division of human embryos into horizons.

These covered the seven weeks of the life of the embryo following which were the fetal stages. Thus each horizon covers one or more days and is correlated to the number of somites which form the basis of the vertebral column.

For the first 25 days or so the human embryo reaches the length of about 4 mm and has 13 to 29 somites. It has no lateral appendages (arms or legs) and no mandibular mouth. Presumably, the skin is very thin and the circulatory and excretory systems are very primitive. This period of the human embryo probably correlates to the early sea-living stage of the primitive vertebrates where they received their body fluid content similar in composition to sea water.

On the 28th day of development arm buds appear on the lateral sides of the embryo in the pectoral region. Leg buds in the pelvic region soon follow. The mandible begins to form. All of these correlate with the fresh water stage of the early vertebrates when they developed a temporary, tough, keratinous skin covering to hold out fresh water from diluting their sea water acquired body fluids. From this rigid skin, spines extended and some of these spines on the lateral surface of the keratinized skin became mobilized and supplied with muscles. Likewise, from the head region of the keratinized skin, a hinged mandibular jaw simultaneously was created in fresh water. Coincidentally was begun the primitive kidney system to selectively excrete waste products and to recover water and elements necessary for nutrition.

In the human embryo soon after this time the lung bud begins as a ventral evagination of the oesophagus. The distal end of the lung bud divides into two parts and eventually each part swings around the oesophagus on either side to produce the lungs in the dorsal portion of the coelomic cavity.

Probably all of the horizons studied in detail by

Streeter, XI to XVIII, represented ancestral fresh water vertebrates. Succeeding these, of course, were those that represented embryonic stages of air-breathing and land-living vertebrates.

Recently, Ronan O'Rahilly, 1973, has completed stages 1 to 10. These correspond somewhat to Streeter's horizons. Probably the earliest of these, stages 1 to 5, conform to the ancestral sea water existence. The development of the amnion should correlate with the amphibian life in fresh water and the development of arms and legs from the ectoderm should predate the origin of the amnion. Consequently there must have been in the human embryo a precocious development of the amnion and allantois with a retardation of the embryo. itself, which receives its arms and legs considerably after it theoretically should. The allantois should correlate to the development of the blastocyst and this to the terrestrial existence of ancestral reptiles and their intermediate descendants.

Apparently, in stage 4, the early blastocyst has formed and begun to implant. This is while the embryo still is in the immature state probably fitting the fresh water existence of amphibians. In the three divisions of stage 5 (implanted but previllous and estimated to be from 7 to 12 days old) the blastocyst becomes well implanted. The yolk-sac may originate in stage 6 as also blood vessel primordia. The allantois begins to appear in stage 7.

Simply stated there appears to have been a speeding up of the unfolding of the extraembryonic membranous housing blastocyst and a retardation of the development of the occupant, the embryo, itself.

The account of the vertebrate lateral appendages appears to be corroborated by Streeter's 1949 description of the arm bud which first appears in embryos having between 21 and 29 paired somites, the two day period which constitutes horizon XII. It originates in the body wall opposite the 5th to 7th cervical somites. He stated "there is no question here as to what is the arm bud itself. It is evident that whatever forces induce it to locate and grow invariably at this site must have been in operation previous to this time. We, therefore, can rule out the spinal nerve roots, which now are just beginning to emerge from the cord. We can also disregard migrant cells to emerge from the somites. The cells of the latter are beginning to break ranks, and a few of them are moving toward the midline to constitute the primordia of the vertebrae. As yet none of these cells can be seen moving into the region of the arm bud. One cannot reject the possibility of accessions from the lining epithelium of the co-elomic tract. But as compared with massive migrations from other coelomic areas, any possible contribution to the arm bud from this source would appear to be trifling. This leaves us, up to this time, but two sources for the pioneer cells of the arm, namely, the overlying skin ectoderm and the unsegmented primary mesoblast of the lateral body wall".

Quite accurately, it might be stated that arms, legs and the jaw are simply external bags of skin into which grew the mesodermal bones, muscles and blood vessels.

DELAYED IMPLANTATION

Hamlett, 1935, discussed delayed implantation of the blastocyst. Ordinarily, fertilization of the ovum takes place usually in the Fallopian tube soon after copulation. Cleàvage goes on as the ova or ovum pass down the tube, and in most species these have already become blastocysts by the time the uterus is reached. Under the control of corpora luteal hormones, implantation occurs soon after. Now at this stage, with the early blastocyst lying near a small patch of implantation decidua in the apex of a simplex uterus, the process of maturation in the armadillo ceases for a period of approximately fourteen weeks. At the end of the period, implantation and growth occur just as abruptly as they had ceased.

Such a situation is known in other mammals and long ago was reported in the roe-deer, *Capreolus,* among the ungulates. Hamlett records that Lataste, 1851, described a similar occurence in five species of rodents, and more recently it has been found to occur in the badger and in albino mice and rats.

There is another type of reproduction cycle which must be differentiated. In some bats, Vespertilionidae and Rhinolophidae, copulation takes place in the fall, the sperms are retained in the uterus through the winter and ovulation occurs the following spring. This is an interval of ovulation following copulation by six or seven months, the actual gestation time being only a few weeks.

Armadillos may produce various numbers of fetuses from one to twelve; all from a single ovum. In South America, Fernandes investigated *Dasypus hybridus* with twelve. In the nine-banded armadillo, a single egg blastocyst implants and there results four more or less identical quadruplets of the same sex.

Further information on this interesting subject may be obtained from Hamlett, Quart, Rev., Biol., 10: 432-447, 1935a.

THE BLASTOCYST

In the first and second half of nearly 700 million years of metazoan life, the ovarian follicle always elaborated only the egg with its yolk supply. The blastocyst is not, nor ever was, created by the ovary. It is produced by the fertilized egg which, instead of directly developing the embryo as before the amphibians, simultaneously fabricated the blastocyst housing along with the development of the embryo.

In the first half of time of animal life on earth the

only extra-embryonic membrane was the yolk sac to enclose the yolk upon which the relatively naked embryo rode usually in water. In the second half since the amphibians and in all descendants (reptiles, birds, monotremes, marsupials and eutherian mammals) the egg itself elaborates membranes in addition to the gut yolk-sac namely, the amnion enclosing the embryo, a second gut sac the allantois and then covers all with the tropoblast to create the blastocyst.

The blastocyst, as a unit, is what implants, either free in the lumen of one tube of a bicornuate uterus or attached by diffuse or local trophoblast erosion of the uterine mucosal wall. *The yolked egg, itself, cannot implant. It must wait until it develops a house for itself and then, in viviparity, the house implants in the uterus. This house is constructed by the egg in the interval between fertilization and implantation.*

In all animals above the fullest evolved amphibians which have the embryo enclosed within the blastocyst, the mother did not provide the housing for the embryo. The embryo was required to build its own house, the blastocyst, from extra-embryonic membranes.

In the final level of eutherian mammalian evolution the bicornuate uterus fused into the simplex uterus where the blastocyst attached interstitially, partially or totally, into the deciduous mucosal wall.

Once implanted, either outside of the maternal body, as in oviparous reptiles, birds and monotremes, or inside as in viviparous reptiles, marsupials and eutherian mammals, the blastocyst normally remains, intact until term.

Nature saw to it that the embryo retained a supreme degree of independence. In the blastocyst the maternal structures did not aid in building the housing for the embryo but compelled the embryo to build its own house. Likewise the embryonic structures were required to manage the physiological functions carried on within the walls of the blastocyst. These were acquisition of nutrition, water and oxygen, storage of waste products and maintenance of the proper amount of fluid in the amniotic cavity. Thus the embryo in its

Fig. 2.—The blastocyst. Redrawn from Sir William Turner. Lectures on the comparative anatomy of the placenta, Edinburgh, 1876.

blastocyst became an active parasite on its mother. On the other hand the maternal tissues also evolved to permit this aggression on the part of the embryo in its blastocyst.

All of this becomes reasonable and obvious when it is realized that during the first 350 million years prior to the development of the blastocyst the naked embryo, riding on its yolk-sac in water, was quite independent of either parents' attention. It was completely on its own. Very little of this self-reliance ever was relinguished in the blastocyst.

When the three germ layers folded ventralward in bilaterally symmetrical, primitive metazoan animals, there was formed an internal, longitudinal gut tube. At the caudal end this opened into an internalward depression of the outside skin in the ventral rear midline. This receptacle also eventually accommodated the reproductive and urinary tract outlets and was known as a cloaca.

This situation continued in both sexes in all anamniote vertebrates including the amphibians. But with the creation by the amphibians of the amniote egg in the blastocyst it became necessary for insemination to occur early in the development and thus by male-female copulation. In the male a portion of the cloaca became modified into an intromissive organ to internally inseminate the egg before the blastocyst covering was placed over it.

With the evolution of the first viviparous mammals, the yolk-sac placental marsupials, the cloaca was longitudinally divided into two tubes, the anterior one accommodating both reproduction and urinary excretion and the posterior tube exclusively for elimination of gut waste products. This may have evolved as a means of preventing fecal infection of the very immature fetus at the time of birth. At any rate this system was employed among all yolk-sac placental marsupials and was presented to the viviparous, allanto-placental eutherian mammals. These mammals used the same conditions of the marsupial male, with two outlets, rectum and urogenital sinus, but in the females the eutherian mammals made an additional separation of the reproductive and urinary tracts so that there were three outlets, as the rule, in the females. Probably these evolutionary changes first occurred in the reptiles immediately ancestral to these two lines of mammals.

In the eutherian mammals there are occasional instances of reversion to the marsupial system (or even farther back to the cloaca).

Although many eutherian mammals adopted the new system, particularly applying to the female with separate rectum, vagina and urethra, some retained one or other of the more primitive arrangements in the perineal region. In artiodactyla and in carnivora the urethra may enter the anterior vaginal wall in the lower third. A few eutherian mammals may go back beyond the marsupials to retain the cloaca, common to reptiles, birds and monotremes.

In many members of Insectivora there is in the female a common outlet for the genital and urinary systems. Walker stated that the insectivorous tenrecs have a cloaca. Eckstein and Zuckerman stated that the female armadillo has an urogenital sinus but that the sloth has a single vagina which has two openings on the perineum. The septum involves the lower third of the vagina.

According to Wood Jones, 1944, there are two eutherian mammals, one carnivore and one insectivore, in which the reproductive outlet systems grossly are very similar in both male and female. The sperms in the male pass into the urogenital sinus and out through the urethra at the end of the penis. In the female the uterus opens into the urogenital sinus and here the only exit is through the urethra, which lies more or less centrally in an enlarged clitoris little differentiated from the male penis. In these two mammals this situation has given rise to much folklore in the sexing of the individuals.

One of these mammals is the spotted hyena, *Crocuta crocuta*. Insemination must occur by tip of the penis to the tip of the clitoris supplied with the urethral canal. The amazing fact is that parturition takes place through the urogenital sinus and out through the urethra. This astonishing anomaly results from continuance of an early stage normal in the embryo.

The other of these anomalous mammals is the European mole, *Talpa europa* which has a very similar gross external genitalia so that proper sexing of an individual is almost impossible. But here in the second spring of life the female perineum becomes highly engorged with blood vessels and an opening appears in the perineum dorsal to the root of the clitoris. This opening extends upwards and into the urogenital sinus and is used for copulation and for parturition. Following the birth of the young the perineal fissure becomes completely closed and the edges fused until the following spring when the process may be repeated.

Early vertebrates including sharks, fishes, amphibians, reptiles and birds had a common external opening, known as a cloaca, to accommodate all three, intestinal excretions, products of reproduction and urinary excretions. This was located ventrally and towards the rear of the body and was a cave-like depression in the skin into which the above named ducts opened.

In the marsupial mammals the cloaca for the first time was divided into a posterior opening for intestinal contents and an anterior vent for products of gestation and urinary excretions. The marsupials had, anterior to the rectum, this urogenital sinus at the apex of which entered the two vaginas and the urethra from the nearby urinary bladder. The male opossum used the female urogenital sinus for introduction of the well developed penis to fertilize the eggs internally. Now the end of this penis was split down the middle for about 1 cm and the canal also was split to allow introduction of sperms into each of the two vaginas which opened into the apex of the urogenital sinus. Above this sinus the two vaginas, one on each side, extending to each of the two uteri, made a wide lateral excursion to go around the ureters, one on each side. This situation was not suitable to allow delivery of the fetuses through them. Consequently all marsupial births occur by a new opening from the uterine cervices directly through the tissues to the apex of the urogenital sinus, thus by-passing the narrow and tortuous vagina on either side.

FROM HOLLOWED-OUT PELVIC FIN RIB TO PENIS

As noted under reproduction in sharks and in viviparous calcareous bony fishes, these primitive vertebrate males, not possessing a penis, make use of a hollowed-out pelvic fin rib to introduce sperms into the female cloaca for internal fertilization. In the sharks these have been modernized into a clasper on each side. This method is common to all sharks and all of the few families of viviparous bony fishes. Almost all of the bony fishes deposit eggs in water where they are externally fertilized and there is no need for male-female copulation.

In the most primitive extant reptile, the New Zealand Tuatara, the males have no copulative organs and internal fertilization of the eggs occurs by application of the male cloaca to that of the female. Turtles, tortoises, crocodiles and alligators have a single, erectile, muscular penis arising from the anterior wall of the cloaca, probably similar to that in some birds. Snakes and lizards have a bilateral pair of such organs, called hemipenes, (plural), hemipenis, (singular) (figure 3), each arising from the root of the tail. They are said not to be homologous with the true penis of other reptiles and of the mammals. Each part may be used independently to internally fertilize the eggs. The one used is related to the position of the copulating individuals.

All reptiles and all birds must have male-female cop-

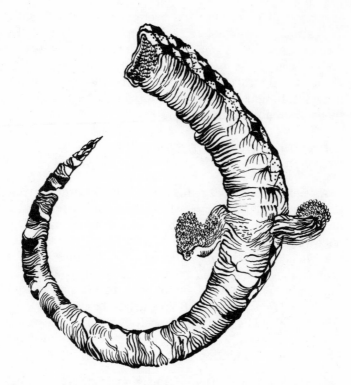

Fig. 3 — Hemipenis in the male Western Gopher snake, *Pituophis melanoleucus*. Specimen from Morris Jackson, illustration by Leslie Dessauer.

ulation to have internally fertilized the eggs prior to the application of the egg shell by the maternal reproductive tract shell gland. For the same reason all invertebrates on land, oviparous or viviparous alike, required internal fertilization by male-female copulation or by the employment of spermatophores, deposited by the male and later picked up by the female. Internal fertilization was necessary prior to the application of the keratinous shell.

While copulation was almost the rule, among a few arthropods copulation proved fatal to the male partner. Among the many thousand species of bees most are solitary. With the highly social honeybee the queen is fertilized while in flight. This is accomplished by a male (drone) in the act of copulation. Since the male intromissive organ remains in the female it is torn away from the male with fatal results to him.

In the spiders the male has antenna-like palps which apply the sperms to the recipient parts of the female. Since this is rather hazardous to the usually smaller male, some such males deposit spermatophores outside of the range of the female. When he departs, the female must come out and pick them up for internal fertilization of the eggs. In the praying mantis the male, in copulating with the female, possibly is unable to release the sperms until the female has eaten off his head.

The mammalian erectile, muscular penis was originated in the reptiles. The peculiar penis of the marsupials is described with reproduction in the marsupials. In the eutherian mammals it is a single median structure through which the urethra extends as in the marsupials. It is distended by arterial blood poured into cavernous veins while the return blood flow is blocked.

According to Matthews, 1941-44, all male bats possess a slender longitudinal bone, known as a baculum, buried in the center of the penis. Such also occurs in many carnivores, notably bears, dogs and raccoons. Possibly this appears in some rodents and in some insectivores.

Bats, because of the position of the lateral skin folds for the wings and tail sheaths, were obliged to face each other in copulation. This may account for the primate-like appearance of the external genitalia of the bats.

INVERTEBRATES AND VERTEBRATES

The invertebrates are the more primitive of the two great divisions of multiple celled, metazoan, animals.

Both were originated and created in the salt water seas where they received body fluids of constitution similar to the sea water and both made use of the variable salts in the sea. Since plant life had preceded them, both migrated to coastal fresh waters where both were required to create an outside keratinous skin casing to hold out fresh water from diluting their sea water acquired body fluids. Both were required to get rid of metabolic waste products. While in sea water each developed a primitive tubular excretory system extending from the internal coelomic body cavity to the outside water. Of necessity to withhold their salt content in fresh water, the excretory systems had to be selective in retaining valuable salts and food elements.

When they migrated to fresh water both groups of animals evolved fins or legs and a hinged predatory mouth in the same fashion and derived from the hard, tough skin casing. This casing was impervious to water and somewhat to oxygen. For respiration some invertebrates and many vertebrates developed gills, vascularized filaments extending into the outside water to secure oxygen. Some invertebrates elaborated fine tubules, tracheae, from the hard skin covering to extend into the body to carry oxygen to the body fluids. The latter was the chief method of arthropods and insects and was readily converted to air which entered these tracheae on land to replace oxygenated water.

The invertebrates got along very well with this exoskeleton in water or in air on land and their progeny became the most numerous of all animals. On the other hand, the vertebrates substituted for this exoskeleton a more or less calcified internal skeleton. Thus the former exoskeleton could be allowed to become soft and pliable and still waterproof to control the body fluid content. Oxygenation principally was by use of vascularized gills extended into oxygenated water.

The invertebrate system readily became converted to use on land but the gill system could not be. Thus the vertebrates finally altered the evaginated gill system to invagination into the thoracic cavity to create the lungs. The lung was first developed by the lungfishes, one of the four direct descendants of the ostracoderms and lived in fresh waters subject to oxygen depletion. In the first amphibians (vertebrates) to come onto land, oxygen perfused inward through their pliable skin from water or on land from air, but the skin had to be kept moist by a mucoid secretion to serve until they developed lungs which they soon borrowed from their cousins the lungfishes.

For reproduction in air on land the invertebrates used the only type of egg known up till then, the simple yolked egg which, to prevent desiccation in air, was supplied with a keratin coat and for fertilization prior to its application in the reproductive tract they adopted male female copulation. The vertebrates never could adapt this simple egg to use on land, but the vertebrate amphibians finally enclosed it in a housing case (the blastocyst) which then was used by all amphibian descendants; reptiles, birds, monotremes, marsupials and eutherian mammals.

At first in both of these divergent groups of metazoan animals while still in sea water, there was no circulation, the body fluids being like a swamp. On transfer to fresh water there became necessary a movement of the body fluids. This was provided by a simple muscularized canal which at intervals pumped the fluid from one end to the other. Later in vertebrates this become a heart, finally with a closed system of arteries and veins joined together by capillaries. Most invertebrates never completed this but have an open circulatory system. However, it became closed in some, for instance, the earthworm and the king crab. When such was accomplished the inner ends of the uriniferous tubules leading from the coelomic cavity were appropriated by tufts of blood vessel capillaries to form the kidney glomeruli.

Henceforth these tubules drained fluid oozing out of the capillaries rather than that collected in the body cavity. These tubules from the coelomic body cavity had previously provided exit for ova or sperms. Now these had to seek other means of escape from the body cavity. The male gonads made an accommodation with the urinary tract for exit of sperms but the female gonad, the ovary, did not. Thus a new ridge from the body cavity wall created an entirely new set of paired tubes leading from the body cavity to the cloaca in the female. This new set of tubes became the Muellerian ducts including the Fallopian tubes, the two horns of the uterus (later joined together into the simplex uterus) and part of the vagina when this more recently was formed by separation of the single cloaca into three perineal openings; anus, vagina and urethra.

Theoretically, no metazoan animal, which originated in the sea as all plants and animals did, could make the step to land without first going through the fresh water stages in which were evolved the methods of maintaining sea water body fluid content on land as all such land animals have done. Of equal significance is the fact that the sudden step from fresh water to land was made very easy because, according to Storer and Usinger, oxygen diffuses from air into tissues 45,000 times as readily as it does from water. It is equally significant that the step from sea water to fresh water could not have been made except for the situation that where sea water joins fresh water there is a wide band of mixing of the two waters. The sea water animals could develop gradually the essential kidney devices necessary to maintain a sea water body fluid content finally ending in fresh water with a fully developed kidney-body-fluid control. This latter was a necessity on land, as was a waterproof skin.

Thus animals were created in the sea from whence

they went to brackish and on to fresh water. In the process they evolved methods of protecting their sea water acquired body fluids. Only then could they come out of water on to land. This last step was facilitated by the physical fact that oxygen is far more easily obtained from air than from water.

In moving from sea water to brackish or fresh water these animals developed a tough and hardened skin covering to prevent fresh water from pouring in to dilute their salt-containing plasma. From this hardened skin extended protective spines some of which became mobilized and supplied with muscles to become fins in fish or arms and legs in the amphibians. From the hardened skin about the head they developed hinged jaws supplied with muscles.

Simultaneously, they evolved tubular excretory organs which became selective in excreting waste products and in recovering useful ones in the filtrate. When the blood circulation developed, capillary tufts entered the mouths of the tubules to form glomeruli and thus the kidneys. Waterproof skin retained the body fluids while the kidneys controlled the contents. This is the situation of all multiple-celled animals in fresh water or in air on land.

The overgrowth of plant life invited the evolution of animals to eat plants. The overgrowth of plant eating animals invited the evolution of carnivores to hold down the population of plant eating animals.

There is a vast gap between the exoskeletonized invertebrates and the internal, mesodermic, usually calcareous skeleton of the vertebrates. But there was one intermediate group of animals which made an attempt to create a mesodermic internal skeleton. These were the echinoderms, originating in sea water, living there today and possessing a thin skin covering. They incorporated calcite crystalline plaques into the mesoderm bound together by the mesodermic cells. Thus they devised rigid hollow tubes generally to the number of five. Their vascular system was and remains extremely simple; they pump oxygenated sea water to their bodies through these tubes. They never could accommodate to fresh water and thus never could come onto land and survive. Their present day descendants inhabit the seas and are represented by sea lilies, starfish, sea urchins, sea cucumbers etc. An excellent, illustrated account of these animals by E. P. F. Rose appears in volume 7 of the *Encyclopedia of the Animal World,* 1972,

EVOLUTION OF A PLACENTA IN THE INVERTEBRATES

In 1938, Snodgrass investigated the anatomy of the walking worm, *Peripatus,* in one of the six subphyla of the PHYLUM ARTHROPODA, the SUBPHYLUM ONYCHOPHORA. This invertebrate, *Peripatus,* here illustrated, is viviparous, as are others in the subphylum. The two linear uteri open above into the coelomic cavity and below into the rectum.. The internally fertilized eggs distribute themselves along the channel in one of the two uteri; each in its own compartment, where it matures and from which it is born as a tiny replica of one of its parents.

Storer and Usinger, 1957, stated that most species of ONYCHOPHORA are viviparous and that in some there is a placenta-like accesory to the maturing embryo through which it obtains nourishment from the uterine wall. If so, this must be the yolk-sac since all invertebrates have a simple yolked egg and no amnion ever develops. The yolk-sac develops from the embryonic midgut to enclose the yolk deposit and is the only extraembryonic membrane. The embryo and its yolk-sac lie free in the uterine secretions, each pair in its own compartment. The embryo receives oxygen through its skin or a later gill system and nutrition from the yolk in the yolk-sac. Now it is possible that when the yolk is exhausted, the yolk-empty yolk-sac

46

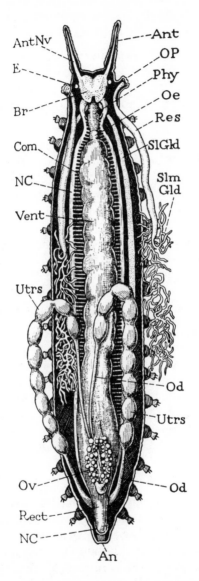

Fig. 4—Ovaries (Ov.), oviducts (Od) and pregnant uteri (Utrs) of the viviparous, invertebrate walking worm, Peripatoides novae zealandiae, Hutton. Duplicated from Snodgrass. Smithsonian Misc. Coll, 97 (No. 6): 1-159, 1938.

47

may remain viable and obtain nutrition from the uterine secretions in which it and the embryo are bathed. Thus a yolk-sac placenta is present.

This is exactly the situation of the viviparous vertebrate shark, in which the yolk-sac, emptied of yolk, still remains vascularized to form a trophonemous organ to continue nutrition to the embryo, secured from uterine secretions.

Thus, the concept of an intervening placental organ occurred early in the invertebrate world and became lodged in the genetic code of all subsequent animals, including the vertebrates, to be revived from time to time and greatly modified. A similar situation took place in respect to respiration. Primitive water-living vertebrates occasionally gulped a bubble of air. Finally the lungfish evolved gills into the chest cavity and breathed air. This became lodged in the genetic code and was very successfully employed by their near cousins, the amphibians and all of their descendants.

The distribution of the gestation cavities along the two uterine horns, here illustrated, was bequeathed not so much to the viviparous sharks but more to the reptiles and the eutherian line of mammals, which employed this method in all multiple gestations in the bicornuate uterus. A major exception occurred in the marsupials, where all multiple gestation sacs lie together in one of the two didelphic uterine cavities.

REPRODUCTION IN SHARKS

The cartilaginous vertebrate sharks were one of the four groups of direct descendants of the ostracoderms in fresh water. The other three were the future marine fishes, the lungfish and the amphibians, all with calcareous bones. All of these animals by then, had closed blood circulations and a relatively stable body fluid content, originally acquired in the salt water seas. In fresh water these were protected against dilution by a water-tight skin and a selective excretory system in the kidneys and this was aided by the gills. Fresh water which these four groups inhabited had occasional periods of suboxygenation. Thus there was a desire for a better oxygenated environment. The efforts in this direction led to the return to the well oxygenated seas on the part of the sharks and marine fishes.

Likewise this led the amphibians to explore habitation in air on land. Of the four groups, only the lungfish remained in these oxygen-depleted fresh waters but it invented the internally placed inverted gill system which originated the lungs.

Naturally, on return to the sea, the sharks and marine fishes were required to modify their body fluid protection systems. Suffice it to state that the two groups used diverse methods. The methods have been described by Paul Budker, 1971, in his volume, *The Life of Sharks*. Homer Smith, 1961, gave a much more complete account. In brief, the sharks evolved an unique system of retention of otherwise very diffusible urea. This was accomplished by modifying the kidneys and gills. Thus their body fluids could be isotonic with the outside sea water.

As to reproduction, the two groups used diverse methods. The teleost, bony fishes produced yolked-eggs in the ovaries and these were expelled to the outside water without much capsule which the sperms could readily pierce for external fertilization. On the other hand, the shark eggs generally were supplied by the maternal ovary with a large quantity of yolk. (In a large oviparous shark this may occupy the space of a large orange). Possibly to hold this together there was added, by the uterine tract shell-glands, a keratinous casing which was impervious to sperms. These egg cases, well illustrated by Budker, had various forms, sometimes flattened like a pea-pod and sometimes corkscrew shaped. Such allowed for tremendous expansion, and some were supplied with tentacles to fasten to seaweeds growing in the water. Some of these had been stated to be up to seven feet long. Consequently, all known sharks required internal fertilization by male female copulation. The male used a hollowed out pelvic fin rib to introduce the sperms into the female cloaca. Evolution of this has produced what is known as a clasper in modern sharks. These are well illustrated by Budker.

The fact that the most primitive oviparous sharks thus required internal fertilization of the eggs may have facilitated the evolution of ovoviparity in the sharks. The eggs confined in the cases could be retained in the maternal reproductive tract until hatching with the fetus born alive. The succeeding step to true viviparity consisted of early fragmentation or complete deletion of the egg case and the embryo and developing fetus could swim free on its yolk-sac within the uterine secretions. This also could permit the yolk depleted yolk-sac to remain vascularized and continue as a placenta acquiring nutrition from the uterine secretions. Such a system of yolk-sac placentation likewise occurred in the invertebrate walking worm and in some of the amphibians.

When any vertebrate animal, anamniote or amniote alike, first achieved viviparity, this major accomplishment in itself usually was enough to permit it to transfer this characteristic in its primitive form to its progeny generally surviving to the present time. However, as soon as viviparity in its simplest form was accomplished, immediately genetic probing in the main line of evolution produced variations also with survival factors and branch animals were given off which also survived to the present time.

Each of these new ideas tended to one thing: more efficient method of nutrition to the embryo-fetus. This may be stated as a general law of zoology and may be demonstrated. Oviparous sharks, nearly 500 million years ago, expelled eggs composed of the embryonic protoplasmic mass plus a tremendous amount of yolk both manufactured by the ovary. These products

THE TWO SORTS OF VIVIPARITY IN VERTEBRATES

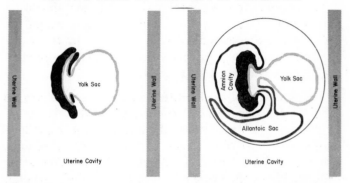

ANAMNIOTE (ABLASTOCYSTIC)

Fig. 5.—

The embryo without covering membranes rides on top of its yolk sac and is oxygenated by uterine secretions.

The embryo is nourished by food stored in the yolk sac plus what it can swallow of uterine gland secretions. Occurs in viviparous fishes, viviparous sharks and viviparous amphibians and also in some viviparous invertebrates.

AMNIOTE (BLASTOCYSTIC)

The embryo is imprisoned in its fluid-filled amniotic cavity and along with its two gut sacs all enclosed within the blastocyst covered by rophoblast.

The embryo is nourished (slightly by yolk sac) but mainly from absorption by trophoblast. Oxygenation is derived from uterine gland secretions. Evolution joined the trophoblast to the uterine wall where oxygen and nutrition came from the maternal blood stream.

Occurrence; primitive stages in viviparous reptiles. Primitive and late stages in marsupial and eutherian mammals.

passed into the oviducts and fertilization took place by internal insemination. In the oviduct the shell gland covered the large-yolked egg with an expansible keratinous membrane which certainly was pervious to oxygen, carbon dioxide, water and electrolytes, and there was no need for a deposit of watery albumen to aid in digesting the yolk. This internally fertilized, shell covered egg was expelled into the sea water in a relatively protected site where it matured.

Ovoviviparity consisted merely in retaining the egg

and shell within the mother's reproductive tract (oviducts) until hatching. In this situation the uterine gland secretions replaced the ocean water, in providing oxygen, water, electrolytes and probably simple chemical compounds.

The second step in reproductive evolution should be elimination of the egg shell. The third step should be reduction in the amount of yolk deposited by the ovary but this would have to correlate with increase in supply of food furnished by the uterus.

The theoretical possibilities in this respect are as follows: (a) the yolk-sac could become a collector of food from outside of its cavity and could grow villous projections into the uterine cavity full of secretions, (b) the umbilical cord could grow villi into the same region and for the same purpose, (c) the embryo could develop faster and acquire early ability to take food by mouth, (d) the uterus could grow vascularized, long villous-like projections from its wall one of which could extend through the spiracle of the embryo and down to its gut tract for constant nutrition and oxygenation. (e) In this respect the precocious embryo could obtain nutrition by eating the eggs subsequently produced by the mother's ovary. (f) As an extreme example the precocious fetus might eat its own brothers and sisters or be eaten by one of them: a true illustration of the survival of the fittest.

Almost every one of these suggestions has been demonstrated to exist in various living sharks. This also may be the pattern for employment in all other groups of anamniote vertebrates: the calcareous bony fishes and the amphibians. The amphibians used all of these as suggested and in addition had many interesting methods of dealing with the oviparous egg.

The sharks had such an efficient body form and their food supply, in a constant ecology, was so plentiful that the body could tolerate almost any fanciful sort of reproduction modifications that had any survival factor and that genetic probing could provide. Thus these peculiar types have survived to this day.

To the above group of possibilities there must be added another one in which is formed a yolk-sac placenta. If so, this must be of the simplest sort of connection of the fetal and maternal tissues, not any more complicated than placentation in viviparous reptiles as well described and illustrated by Weekes, 1925-1935. Such is as follows: the fetal and maternal capillaries approach each other by degeneration of and flattening of the maternal and fetal epithelial surfaces, but there is no loss of the epithelia. The fetal epithelial cells in rare instances possess microvillous projections that are insinuated between the maternal epithelial cells thus creating a simple union. It seems that more than this would be impossible without some decidual reaction. And decidual reaction was not to be invented for several hundred million years and then only half way up in the eutherian mammalian reproductive evolution.

Since they were among the originators of anamniote vertebrate viviparity, the sharks had their own particular type of reproduction within the group. Each succeeding stage apparently was successful in producing families which extended to the present time and with little variation of the stage mechanism.

Moreover all succeeding groups of anamniote vertebrates should follow the same stages and in the same order. Thus the calcareous bony fishes and the amphibians each should follow the same scheme although in these the original shell membrane had been lost and the original large quantity of yolk had been remarkedly reduced probably coordinate with an early development of a fetus which could obtain nutrition by mouth from the uterine gland secretions.

The sharks were unique in that they developed all

theoretically possible modifications of reproduction based upon the anamniote egg. These variations included oviparity, ovoviviparity and true viviparity with the development of the first true placenta (epitheliovitelline, yolk-sac, placenta).

Mahadevan, 1940, summarized the gestation processes in the following words: "Viviparity among the elasmobranchs is by no means uncommon. As stated by R. W. Shann (1925) three general methods of nutrition of the young may be said to be in vogue. Either the yolk-sac forms a pseudo-placental connection with the uterine wall as in *Scoliodon sorrokowah, Scoliodon walbeehmi, Scoliodon palasorrah, Hemigalcus balfouri* and *Mustelus laevis,* or the uterine wall secretes a nutrient fluid which is absorbed by means of external gill filaments, or again, the uterine wall itself is produced into long secretory villi or papillae, which enter the alimentary canal of the embryo by way of the spiracles.

"According to the mode of obtaining nourishment certain structures are developed by the parent fish as well as by the embryos during the different periods of intra-uterine existence. In the placental forms as in *S. palasorrah* and *S. walbeehmi,* in the earlier embryonic stages, a placenta is absent, the yolk in the yolk-sac being the main source of nourishment. But as pregnancy advances the yolk gets absorbed and a placenta is developed by the modification of the yolk-sac and then nourishment is obtained through the blood vascular system.

"In *Carcharinus dussumieri* no yolk-sac placenta is at all developed due to the large amount of yolk in the yolk-sac which provides nourishment for the growing embryos during a greater part of their intra-uterine development. In *S. sorrakowah,* on the other hand, the yolk present being very poor, the embryo is compelled

54

to obtain nourishment by other ways and so the placenta is established very early in development.

"In the placental Elasmobranchs, the Rays and Skates, the yolk-sac persists, the yolk being taken directly into the alimentary canal. In some cases an internal yolk-sac is also present. The blood vessels in the mesoblastic portion of the yolk-sac are also of use in absorbing the nourishment contained within it. External gill filaments present in the early stages of the embryos also help in absorption. Southwell and Prasad (1919) have mentioned that in some forms certain special processes, the trophonemata, are developed which enter the embryonic spiracles and pour secretion into the pharynx.

"In most species of *Scoliodon* special structures, the appendicula, are developed on the placental cord as in *S. sorrakowah, S. palasorrah* and *S. walbeehmi.* These are simple, long and filamentous and rarely branched in *S. sorrakowah,* much branched in *S. palasorrah,* very short and branched in *S. walbeehmi* and entirely absent in *Carcharinus dussumieri.* The function of these is to help in the absorption of the uterine secretion.

"In the sharks the different parts of the oviduct are functionally modified, for, although the ova are fertilized within the oviduct, the development of the young is not carried out in invariably the same plan, some being fully developed and born alive, while in others the ova are encased in a horny covering and deposited in the sea where they undergo a protracted development".

In the large oviparous forms the quantity of yolk deposited by the ovary along with the microscopic embryonic protoplasm was enormous, approaching that of the large, primitive, amnioblastocystic eggs of large reptiles and birds evolved 150 million years later. During the interval no other placenta ever occurred.

In the viviparous forms of sharks the yolk quantity was greatly diminished. In the sharks both ovaries develop to function as likewise, both uterine horns with ostia opening into the abdomen cavity. The long uterine horns join together and open in a single orifice into the common midline cloaca. Gestations occur along each uterus and sometimes are each in its own compartment made by folds of the uterine mucosa. Near the ostium is located the 3 or 4 mm long shell gland on each side. No mention is made of uterine glands but the succulent mucosa is folded into ridges and valleys.

Springer, 1948, described the oviphagus embryos common to the Sand Shark, *Carcharias taurus*. Not only the right ovary but both uteri were developed and each of the latter had one embryo, each measuring a little more than 10 inches long. Along with them, free in their uteri, were numerous egg capsules and a considerable number were empty and the stomachs of the embryos were distended with egg yolk and an occasional intact ovum but no egg capsules. (As a modification of this, some shark embryos may have been cannibalistic).

Mahadevan described in detail the placentation of *Scoliodon palasorrah* of which she had 12 specimens containing 29 embryos, and a couple with early blastocysts. The eggs from paired ovaries grow to comparatively large size, 3 or 4 mm in diameter. The two uteri are divided into as many compartments as there are embryos, generally two on each side. An embryo or fetus, 270 mm long, was found in one specimen showing that it may attain greater length. The tail is usually folded back to one side.

Following is Mahadevan description of the placenta in this species. "The most advanced stage of placenta studied shows a much folded yolk-sac devoid of any yolk, whose connection with the trophonemous cup is very intimate and firm. Even here a part of the yolk-sac is free and does not enter the cup. This free part of the yolk-sac in section, now shows a very well-developed active epithelium (illustrated). The cells are poly-nuclear and are uniformly long and columnar and granulated, with spherical nuclei. The nuclei are mostly terminal and very chromatic. The cells project freely to the outside, and in some, the tips are rounded off and these along with their nuclei, get cut off and thrown into the lumen. The mesoderm does not show much change, but the blood vessels have increased in size and are not quite so numerous. The vessels crossing the lumen have increased greatly not only in number but also in size. Internally there is a thin endodermal layer.

"The lumen of the yolk-sac now is devoid of any yolk granules or albuminous coagulated matter but is traversed by numerous blood vessels. In many places, the sac is so much folded that the sides of two folds come together and are connected to each other by connective tissue, blood vessels, etc.

"The trophonematous cup in the advanced stage is very large and very well developed. The foetal tissue advances and closely lines the uterine villi, and the arrangement becomes more regular. To increase the surface of contact, each fold becomes pilately branched, the structure therefore becoming more complex. In between the villi, the spaces are filled with blood vessels, the largest of these occurring in the center of the cup. At this stage a trophonemoous villus, together with the enveloping fold of the yolk-sac shows the following changes. The core of mesoblast has become very narrow and is traversed by blood vessels and is followed by a very well developed vascular region. The epiphelial layers of both maternal and foetal tissues consist of very few flat cells with flat nuclei, and the intervening space between the two is extremely narrow, or almost absent. Thus (a) an increase and enlargement of the maternal and foetal capillaries to meet the increasing demands of the growing embryo, (b) the attenuation of the uterine epithelium and also of the foetal yolk-sac epithelium, and (c) the pronounced bulging of the maternal and foetal capillaries over the placental face with their own walls reduced in thickness are the most important changes that take place in the maternal and foetal tissues so as to bring about a close apposition of the maternal and foetal blood streams".

In her summary Mahadevan stated "the yolk-sac placenta is formed by the modified spongy yolk-sac getting embedded in the trophonemous cup. In the placenta, though foetal tissue is attached to the maternal tissue, there is no invasion of the maternal tissue by the foetal tissue".

In the sharks the uterine mucosa apparently had not yet formed glands. Instead there were vascularized villous projections which may be considered to be essentially everted glands. The modification of these was extensive, some forming trophonema fitted to the fetal vascularized yolk-sac, as in this case, and others forming long villous-like shreads of uterine mucosa to enter the fetal spiracle to the pharynx.

It is postulated that sharks diverge from teleost fishes in so many ways that they can no longer be considered to be fishes, no more than can whales or dolphins be so classified. Just as the amphibians arose coordinate with fishes and sharks, these three entities should be differentiated from the time of their origin from the fresh water ostracoderms.

REPRODUCTION IN FISHES

In reproduction the calcareous, bony, vertebrate fishes varied from the cartilaginous vertebrate sharks in several respects. The shark embryo required a long time to mature. Therefore the eggs had a large quantity of yolk and a firm keratinous casing to retain it. Thus the sperms could not pierce the shell and internal fertilization by male female copulation was requisite prior to the application of the shell by the maternal uterine shell gland.

The fish embryo, on the other hand, matured rapidly into a tiny replica of the adult and then could shift for itself. A relatively smaller quantity of yolk sufficed with a more pervious membrane covering. This could be penetrated by the sperms in the surrounding water and internal fertilization was unnecessary. For the most part the fishes then remained oviparous with external fertilization in water but even here there were some evolutionary tendencies.

Primarily myriads of eggs thus were deposited but the maturity rate was low. Eventually in some families a lesser number of eggs were produced but better care was taken by the parents. Some (sticklebacks) made a crude nest of hollowed out sand or pebbles below the shallow water. Here the eggs were deposited, externally fertilized and the male guarded the nest during incubation of the eggs. Other families developed a skin pocket on one or the other parent for incubation of the eggs (sea horse and immaturely in the pipefish). In some catfish the eggs were held in the male or female parent's mouth for incubation. A very few families evolved viviparity either by retention of the eggs in the maternal reproductive tract or in the ovary until maturity of the fetus when it escaped through the maternal cloaca.

All of these procedures were in the repertory of the theoretical methods of management of the simple yolked egg then in vogue. All of these various systems at one place or another were employed by the invertebrates and the primitive vertebrates (sharks, fishes and amphibians) which had no other than the simple yolked egg for reproduction. This egg is illustrated in figure 1; A, 1, 2, 3.

Among the 33 orders of fishes, viviparity is confined to a few orders, the principal one being Cyprinodontes. C. L. Turner, 1933-1940, investigated the peculiar type of viviparity in these fish in the number of species in the following families. Poeciliidae, 38, Anablepidae, 2, Goodeidae, 24, and Jenynsiidae, 1. Most of these possess a minute quantity of yolk and the embryo develops an inadequately vascularized yolk-sac and apparently is obliged to vascularize other embryonic tissues to secure enough oxygen and nutrition for development. These tissues vary from family to family but do have some relationship. In all of the species in this order of fishes the internally fertilized egg develops within its ovarian follicle where it remains until hatching in all species of Poeciliidae and of Anablepidae. In all species of Goodeidae and of Jenynsiidae the ovarian follicle degenerates and the embryos are expelled into a common ovarian cavity. In either case, the wall of the follicle or of the common ovarian cavity becomes highly maternally vascularized to provide oxygen, water and nutrition to the developing embryos.

In some of these there is radical modification of the orthodox method in obtaining these three elements necessary for growth. In some with reduced supply of yolk the embryonic portal system instead of concentrating upon vascularizing the yolk-sac transfers its vascularization to the near-by pericardial sac presumably for more oxygenation while the yolk-sac atrophies. This pericardial sac then enormously enlarges producing an anteriorly attached herniated sac which almost surrounds the anterior end and head of the fetus. The ventral wall surface of this sac is extensively fetally vascularized to receive nutrition and oxygen from the likewise extensively maternally vascularized wall of the ovarian follicle. Here they remain throughout gestation. This is characteristic of those fish embryos which remain until hatching within the individual ovarian follicle. These include species of the two families, *Poeciliidae* and *Anablepidae*.

In two other families, *Goodeidae* and *Jenynsiidae*, the follicles degenerate and the embryos are expelled into a common cavity in the single ovary. Here oxygen, water and nutrition are supplied to the living embryo by exudation of oxidated nutrient fluid from the extensively vascularized ovarian cavity wall. In addition nutrition is acquired from the autolyzed bodies of nearly half of the embryos which failed to survive. In species of *Goodeidae* a supplementary method of nutrition is employed. The vascular ovarian cavity wall is thrown up into folds and villous-like projections. One of the processes enters the gill aperture of the embryo and extends downward into the esophagus and forward into the mouth from which it may protrude. This is similar to the embryonic nutrition in the primitive shark family, the Butterfly Ray, *Pteroplatea* which differs in that the vascularized trophonemata emerge from the mucosal wall of the uterus, enter the spiracles of the embryos and in each extends to the esophagus. If the mode of reproduction were known in all anamniote animal species a similar procedure of embryo-fetal nutrition may be found to be not too rare. Such could not occur in viviparous reptiles or in mammals where the embryo is imprisoned in its amniote sac which in turn, with the fetal membranes, all are enclosed within the blastocyst.

In the family, *Jenynsiidae* there is another unique method of oxygenating and feeding the embryo-fetus. The latter develops long, fetal vascularized, external projections from its anal region. These, covered with gut endothelium, extend into the surrounding fluid contents of the ovarian cavity where they presumably acquire oxygen and nutrition. Since these are lined by endothelium and extend from the lower gut region

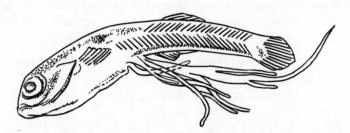

Fig. 6.—Accessory respiratory or nutritive organ extending from anal region of an embryo of **Zoogonecticus cuitzeoensis.** Redrawn from 'Viviparity in the Goodeidae' by C. L. Turner. Plate one, J. Morph. 55: 207-251, 1933-34. Length of embryo, 10.5 mm. The processes were covered by gut entoderm.

they may be forerunners of the allantoic sac first occurring in the blastocyst common to reptiles, birds and mammals.

There also is another restricted group of fishes, a family of the blennies, which has on orthodox method of viviparous reproduction. The embryos develop in the maternal reproductive channel, unlike the cyprinodonts with ovarian gestation, but like the viviparous sharks. All viviparous fishes must practice male female copulation and insemination is said to be by use of a hollowed out pelvic fin rib inserted into the female cloaca as in all sharks.

LAMPREYS AND HAGFISHES

Some 700 million years ago, the first animal life was in a single nucleated cell evolved from a nucleated plant cell. Reproduction was by simple fission into two cells. Soon the repeated cell divisions created cells that remained together to form sheets of tissue. Eventually there were three superimposed sheets. These three sheets as a unit folded ventralward to mold the embryo. The top sheet formed the ectodermic skin of the embryo, the middle sheet formed the mesodermic muscles, bones and circulatory system and the lowest sheet formed the gut canal which extended out a sac to surround the yolk supply of food for the embryo. Between the mesoderm and the entodermic gut was a space called the coelomic cavity. From bilateral ridges in the lining of this cavity arose the ovaries or testes which expelled ova or sperms into the coelomic cavity. Simultaneously and while still in salt water, there were bilateral rows of tubules leading from the coelomic cavity to the outside. These tubules drained metabolic waste products which had collected from the sluggish body fluids into the coelomic cavity. Likewise these uriniferous tubules served as exits for ova or sperms. Body fluids were the same in content of salts as the surrounding sea water.

Some such primitive vertebrates migrated to the coastal fresh waters where, in order to exist, they were obliged to create a tough, keratinous skin to hold out fresh water from diluting the salts of their body fluids. Eventually, they mobilized spines protruding from the outside keratinized casing to provide fins (later to become legs, arms or wings). From the hardened skin about the mouth they created a rigid, hinged jaw.

These were the ostracoderms in fresh water and when completed these fresh-water vertebrates gave origin to four diverse groups, (1) lungfishes, (2) sharks, (3) marine fishes, and (4) amphibians. The lungfishes remained in these, frequently oxygen depleted, waters, but developed lungs and periodically breathed air. The sharks and marine fishes went back to the well-oxygenated salt water seas, while the amphibians came on land.

There can be little doubt that the lampreys and hagfishes evolved from the early ostracoderms after they had obtained a tough, keratinous skin in fresh water but before the ostracoderms had produced fins and a rigid, muscularized jaw. From this half-way stage, the lampreys and hagfishes evolved in fresh water but went back to the well oxygenated salt water seas. There they retained their original cylostome (sucker) mouth but were without fins. They grovelled in the bottom mud for plant and invertebrate food. But when the sharks and marine fishes much later returned to the sea water, then, these primitive vertebrates found a new ecology to exploit. From the keratinous casing about the cyclostome mouth sharp teeth-like projections on a rasping tongue were developed. So equipped, these primitive fish attach themselves to the body of a marine fish, incise a hole in its skin and subsist upon the body fluids drained from the host. Thus, these parasitic vertebrates survived for possibly 500 million years.

As in most fishes, their mode of reproduction was by eggs deposited in water to be fertilized by male sperms and to mature there.

Thus, the lampreys and hagfishes may be considered to have originated (as all other animals) in salt sea water (to obtain their sea water acquired body fluids and their cyclostome mouth). Then their ancestors migrated to fresh water where was acquired a keratinized fresh water repelling skin but no fins or rigid mouth. At this point they returned to the sea. As in some of the sharks, their body fluids appear to be protected either in salt water or in fresh water. Thus their mode of control must be readily reversible.

A still more primitive vertebrate was the sea water lancelet, *Amphioxus*, without fins but possessed of a cyclostome mouth surrounded by many gill filaments. In place of a vertebral column this primitive sea animal had a notochord. It reproduces by externally fertilized eggs with the embryo developing into a larval stage prior to metamorphosis. Probably the primitive seas were well populated by thin-skinned, finless and jawless cyclostomes indigenous to the seas but when the sharks and marine fishes, with fins and predatory jaws, reentered the seas from fresh water, where these appendages were developed, the defenseless cyclostome vertebrates soon were annihilated, with the exception of *Amphioxus* which possibly saved itself from extinction by its habit of burrowing into sand underneath the water.

REPRODUCTION IN AMPHIBIANS

According to the classification of amphibians presented by M. K. Hecht in the *Enclycopaedia Britannica,* 1972, the class of amphibia was divided into two subclasses, Apsidospondyli (with vertebrae performed in cartilage and later changed to bone) and subclass, Lepospondyli (amphibians with vertebrae not preformed in cartilage).

The first subclass, Apsidospondyli, had two superorders, Labyrinthodontia and Salienta. Of the Labyrinthodontia there were four orders all of which became extinct prior to the Cenozoic era. Romer, in his *Vertebrate Paleontology,* 1966, illustrated the oldest known amphibian skeleton, Ichthyostege, about three feet long and of the late Devonian. The other superorder, Salienta (frogs and their relatives) had about 19 families, which have descendants existing at the present time.

Coleman J. Goin presented a lecture on the amphibians before the 38th annual banquet of the American Society of Ichthyologists and Herpetologists and this was published in the Annual Report of the Smithonian Institution, 1959. The author graciously has given me permission to quote extensively from this paper, since the facts are so condensed that it would be impractical to attempt an abstract. The following represent many of the families of the superorder, salienta. (order Anura).

"*Pipidae* — Three types of life history are exempli-

65

fied by the very aquatic frogs of the family Pipidae. In the Old World forms, such as the African clawed frog, *Xenopus,* the eggs are deposited in the water and are attached to weeds. On the other hand, in the five American species, including the Surinam toad, *Pipa pipa,* eggs are placed in pouches on the backs of the females. These pouches are temporary pits formed in the soft skin of the dorsum. Development is direct in two species and probably also in a third, but in the other two the eggs hatch into tadpoles that resemble those of the Old World species.

"*Discoglossidae* — The mating behavior of the obstetrical toad, *Alytes obstetricans,* has been worked out in rather careful detail. The males call from small holes in the ground. Mating occurs on the ground nearby and is apt to last most of the night. The male clasps the female tightly around the head above the forelimbs and gently massages her cloacal region with his toes. Just before the eggs are laid, the male moves his hind legs forward so that his heels are together anterior to and above the cloaca of the female. As the eggs are emitted the male catches the mass in his feet and by stretching his legs backward, delivers from 20 to 60 eggs which the female expels with a sudden noise. The male then moves his legs around, entwining the eggs about his legs. He carries them for several weeks, until the tadpoles are about ready to hatch, at which time he makes a brief visit to a pool where no other tadpoles are present. Here he deposits the eggs; the little tadpoles hatch out and finish their development as tads in the pool.

"*Bombina maxima,* the yellow-bellied toad, breeds in the water. The male clasps the female just above the front of the hind limbs and the eggs are laid in small masses which, instead of being wrapped around the legs of the male, sink to the bottom or come to rest suspended on submerged vegetation. Here they lie until the eggs hatch.

"Rhinophrynidae — The Mexican burrowing toad, *Rhinophrynus,* exhibits an aquatic courtship, the males grasping the females in front of the hind legs. The eggs are then deposited in the water where they hatch out in aquatic larvae which later undergo metamorphosis.

"Leptodactylidae — The two abundant genera of New World leptodactylids, *Leptodactylus,* the nest-building frogs, and *Eleutherodactylus,* the robber frogs, have rather uniform life histories among themselves. The species of *Leptodactylus* build frothy nests in or near bodies of water. The eggs are deposited and hatch within these nests. The larvae have very slim bodies and make their way through the nest to the adjacent water. While there is some variation in larval form among the different species, in general throughout the genus there is agreement of nest form and larval habits. A few leptodactylids have become more terrestrial. *L. nanus* scoops out a small basin in the earth at a site some distance from the water. The froth and eggs are deposited in this basin which is then roofed over with mud. A tiny aperture is left at the top through which the young escape after metamorphosis.

"Eleutherodactylus lays its eggs on land. Here, about sunrise in the morning, generally under stones or logs or similar cover, the female deposits her eggs while clasped by the male who fertilizes them as they are deposited. These eggs go through direct development and at hatching the little froglet is a miniature replica of the adult.

"Life histories of *Paludicola* and *Eupemphix* are similar in pattern to that characteristic of *Leptodactylus.* *Zachaenus,* like *L. nanus,* lays its eggs in an earth basin, but the basin is not roofed over. The young, however, complete metamorphosis in the basin as do the young of *L. nanus.*

"In the Australian *Heleioporus eyrei,* the eggs are

67

laid in a frothy mass of jelly underground in the spring of the year. Development proceeds within the egg until the external gills have been lost and the gill covering developed. Hatching seems to depend on the nest being flooded.

"The Australian *Limnodynastes tasmaniensis* lays small eggs which are enclosed in a gelatinous frothy mass floating on any available water supply. These eggs hatch in about 48 hours and the newly emerged larvae make their way from the frothy mass into the water where they immediately attach themselves to water plants, debris, or other submerged objects.

"*Centrolenidae* — Not too much is known concerning the breeding habits of this distinctive little family of tree frogs. The eggs are deposited in disklike masses on the undersides of green leaves. These masses are invariably above running water, into which the tadpoles fall on hatching. It has been reported for *Cochranella fleischmanni*, of Barro Colorado Island, Panama Canal Zone, that the easiest way to locate the frogs is to search out the egg masses. At night a male will nearly always be in attendance. Multiple matings by a single male have been reported for this species.

"*Bufonidae* — The true toads, like so many other anuran families, show a diversity of life histories. In the genus *Bufo* the males go to the ponds in spring, in the Northern Hemisphere at least, and give their calls. When the female approaches the male, the latter embraces her behind the front legs and the pair float at the surface, the male leaving his hind legs hanging free. As the female deposits the eggs, the male brings his knees to rest in her groin with heels almost touching. The female pushes along the bottom and deposits strings of small-yolked eggs, which may number in the thousands. They hatch in 2 to 4 days into little, short, polliwog-type tadpoles. These tadpoles transform into tiny toads a month or two later.

"In the African genus *Nectophrynoides,* which contains but three species, the eggs are not laid but are retained in the body of the female where they hatch; the young go through their larval development in the oviducts of the mother. The number of young is greatly reduced in comparison to the number produced by the toads that lay their eggs in water, but even so, more than 100 may be taken from a single female of *Nectophrynoides vivipara.* Despite the fact that these larvae remain in the oviduct rather than having a free-living tadpole stage, few of the important characters of tadpoles have actually been lost. Transformation takes place within the oviduct and fully developed young are born. No copulatory organs have been described for this genus of frogs, and how the spermatazoa are transmitted from the male to the female is not known".

(*NOTE*) It may be added here that Nectophrynoides makes another perfect example of how animals, prior to the evolution of the blastocyst, used the simple yolked egg with the naked embryo riding on its yolk-sac, to produce viviparity. Instead of living in the water of seas or lakes, the embryo matured protected in the watery confines of the mother's uterus where it swam in secretions as it did when developed in water. Its nutrition came principally from the yolk but it could take in secretions by mouth and its oxygen perfused through its skin or gills from oxygenated maternal secretions. Similar use of the simple yolked (anamniote) egg occurred in the viviparous, invertebrate walking worm, *Peripatus.* Another example occurred in the viviparous, vertebrate sharks. Other instances among the amphibians are *Salamandra atra, Hydromantes, Oedipus, Proteus* and in the caecilian *Gymnophis* and *Geotrypetes.*

Goin continues:

"*Rhinodermatidae* — The small Andean Darwin's frog, *Rhinoderma darwini,* has one of the most unusual of all life histories known among the frogs. Several males will watch a clutch of 20 to 30 eggs, deposited on land by a single female, for 10 to 20 days, until they are nearly ready to hatch and the embryos can be seen moving inside them. Over a period of several days.

each male then picks up a number of eggs, one at a time, with his tongue and slides them down into his vocal pouch. Here the young pass the larval stage. They do not emerge until metamorphosis is completed. Although it lacks a free-living larval period, the developing frog is for a time completely tadpolelike.

"The tiny *Sminthillus limbatus* of Cuba lays one large-yolked egg on land which hatches into a fully formed frog.

"*Dendrobatidae* — The little poison frogs are apparently rather uniform in the fact that the male carries the tadpoles on his back until he deposits them in a body of quiet, casual water. In *Dendrobates auratus*, the male has no definite calling site but makes a low buzzing sound as he moves about over the ground on a morning after a rain. Usually a male will be followed by several females, some of which will actually jump on him. He is apparently aware of his admirers because if pursuit lags, he slows down and becomes more vociferous. Finally he dives beneath the wet leaf mold and is followed by a female. The details of mating are not known and in fact it is not even sure that it does take place under these situations. It is known, however, that the female lays on land from one to six rather large-yolked eggs which are surrounded by an irregular, sticky, gelatinous material with no definite external film. These eggs hatch in about 2 weeks. The male either guards or visits the clutch, and the newly hatched tadpoles wiggle onto his back. Some time later he moves to the water and the tadpoles slide off. Tadpole-carrying males have been noted in trees quite some distance from water, although it may be that they were carrying tadpoles up to tree holes which contained water. Tadpoles collected in water have been known to live for a least 42 days before transformation. Similar habits are shown by the related genera, *Phyllobates* and *Prostherapis*, although apparently the number of tadpoles carried by an individual male is greater. In *Phyllobates,* males have been found carrying as many as 15 tadpoles, and tadpole-carrying males of this genus have been seen as far as a quarter of a mile from water. A specimen of *Prostherapis fuliginosus* has been taken with 25 tadpoles on the back.

"*Atelopodidae* — As far as I know, the brightly colored little toads of this family exhibit aquatic breeding habits with indirect development—that is, the eggs are laid in water and pass through a tadpole stage before transformation.

"*Hylidae* — The tree frogs have very diverse life histories. One group comprises a few genera of South American frogs placed together in the subfamily Hemiphractinae. These include *Cryptobatrachus, Hemiphractus, Gastrotheca,* and *Amphignathodon.* While typically hylid in appearance, these frogs have the habit of carrying eggs in a mass on the back of the female. In some, this mass is imbedded in or covered by a fold of skin which forms a veritable sac as in the marsupial frog *Gastrotheca marsupiata.* In others, such as *Cryptobatrachus evansi,* the female carries the eggs exposed on the back where they go through their development. In other hylids assigned to the subfamily Hylinae, the life history is less modified, but even here there are specializations. In the Central and South American genus *Phyllomedusa,* for example, the male clasps the female while she moves about through the trees and selects a leaf over water on which to deposit her eggs. While spawning, the pair move slowly forward from the tip of the leaf toward the stalk, folding the leaf into a nest and filling it with eggs and foam. The two ends of the leaf are left open. In this foamy mass the eggs develop into tadpoles which then fall through the hole in the end of the leaf into the water below. In *Hyla decipiens* likewise the eggs are laid in a gelatinous mass on a leaf

71

overhanging sluggish water. Upon hatching, the larvae break free and fall into the water.

"*Hyla rosenbergi* and *Hyla faber* build basins of mud on or near the edge of pools. In these basins they deposit their eggs. The tadpoles have enormous gills with which they adhere to the surface film of these basins. With the rise of water following the rains, the tadpoles make their way into the body of the pool or stream.

"In *Hyla goeldi* the eggs are carried on the back of the female until ready to hatch, at which time the mother goes and sits in the water while hatching progresses.

"In Jamaica, all the species of *Hyla* have specialized breeding habits. They deposit their eggs in the little water held at the base of leaves of "wild pines" or bromeliads. Here the little tadpoles hatch out and start through their development. Food is quite scarce in this environment and the tadpoles have become specialized for feeding upon the eggs laid either by the mother or some other female. In some forms, at least, they may eat the eggs of other species, but certainly in *Hyla brunnea* it can be demonstrated that they eat the eggs of their own species, for in certain parts of the Blue Mountains where I have observed this behavior, *brunnea* is the only *Hyla* present. Not only do the tadpoles eat the eggs of their own species, but, in all probability, they eat the tadpoles of the same clutch. As one watches a developing nest, in the early stages there are many tadpoles present, but as time goes on the tadpoles become fewer and fewer, so that by the time transformation is about to take place perhaps less than half a dozen living tadpoles are left to transform. The reduction in teeth and the extremely long tails of these tadpoles are presumably modifications for existence in this environment. Similar egg-eating tadpoles have been described for a continental genus of hylid, *Anotheca*, of Mexico and Central America.

"Many of the hylas do, however, have the habit of breeding in open water with the unprotected eggs transforming through the tadpole stage into little frogs. In the gray treefrog, *Hyla versicolor*, for example, the adults go to the ponds from April to early summer to breed. The eggs are laid, scattered in small masses or packets of not more than 20 to 40 eggs each, on the surface of quiet pools. These packets are loosely attached to the vegetation. The egg itself is but slightly larger than a millimeter in diameter while the outer envelopes may be more than 4 mm. in diameter. The eggs hatch in 4 to 5 days and the tadpoles emerge to swim around and feed in the pond for about a month and a half to 2 months until they transform, usually in the middle or late summer, into small frogs that may be from 15 to 20 mm. in snout-to-vent length.

"*Ranidae* — The typical life-history pattern of the so-called "true frogs" of the genus *Rana* is too well known to deserve more than passing mention. In *Rana pipiens*, the leopard frog, the eggs are laid in the spring months. They are deposited in large masses attached to submerged plants, twigs, or sticks, or they may even rest on the bottom, unattached, in open ponds and marshes. After hatching, the tadpole exists as a sunfish-type tadpole with a very high tail fin for 2 or 3 months. The tadpole itself is quite large and often exceeds 3 inches in length.

"A couple of Oriental species of *Rana* lay their eggs out of water on leaves or stones or even in the mud near the bank, but these egg masses are essentially unmodified and the larvae which escape from them soon make their way into the water. This habit of laying its eggs out of water is also found in the South African genus *Phrynobatrachus*. All the species of *Staurois*, a genus characteristic of mountain-torrent regions of southeastern Asia, lay their eggs in the pools below the cascades. These eggs hatch out in aquatic

73

tadpoles that are especially adapted for life in mountain torrents by having large suctorial disks back of the mouth.

"In the genus *Cornufer* of the East Indies we find the extreme modification in ranid development in that, instead of hatching out into tadpoles which later metamorphose, development is carried on in the eggs which are laid on land and which hatch out directly into fully formed tiny froglets.

"*Rhacophoridae* — The Old World tree frogs typically lay their eggs in masses of foam on the leaves of plants or other structures above the water. The habits of *Rhacophorus leucomystax* may be taken as an example. The breeding season is apparently very long, egg foam having been collected from late April through August. The breeding places include the walls of unused manure pools and sometimes the crops in flooded fields. If no suitable pool or other water is available, the egg foam may be laid on the ground during rainy evenings. During the process of egg laying, the female does most of the work of producing the foam mass. Before the eggs appear she ejects a small amount of fluid, and this she beats into a froth by moving her feet medially and laterally and turning them as she crosses them on the midline. When the foam for holding the eggs has been prepared, the eggs and the fluid come out together. During the egg-laying process, the male is passive, grasping the female under the armpits and simply holding his body closely applied to her back, his eyes half closed. His pelvic region is bent down with the cloacal opening near that of the female. Apparently the eggs are fertilized as they leave the cloaca of the female. When the egg-laying process has been completed, the female stands up on her forelimbs and the male tries to get away from the foam in which the distal ends of his hind legs are buried. The female usually gets away from the foam later by moving her legs and body sideways with the help of large sticky finger disks. The foam is white at first but in a few moments changes to light brown. The eggs, which are without pigmentation, are scattered singly or in small groups in the big foam mass but are mostly concentrated near the basal part where the foam is attached to the substrate. The incubation period apparently varies with the temperature, and in some cases has been known to take from 6 to 7 days. The tadpoles also hatch in different stages of development. Some of the newly hatched individuals have external gills fully exposed while others have their external gills partly covered by the operculum and are much more heavily pigmented. Near the time of hatching, the foam containing the embryos begins to liquefy and the active movement of the fully developed embryos or tadpoles in the liquefied foam drops them into the water below. Sometimes the whole egg foam mass with its contained tadpoles may be washed down by rain into the pool below. When the liquefied foam drops into the water the tiny bubbles in it disappear and the tadpoles swim actively in the water. A few rhacophorids lack the habit of "egg beating." For example, African frogs of the genus *Hyperolius* lay their eggs in small clusters directly in the water. *Kassina* is apparently quite closely related to *Hyperolius,* and it likewise lacks the habit of "egg-beating." Its eggs are small and pigmented and laid singly or in pairs in the water.

"Microhylidae — In the narrow-mouthed toad, *Microhyla carolinensis*, the eggs are pigmented, firm, and rather distinctively shaped. The complement ranges from 700 to 1,000 eggs which float at the surface film. The tiny tadpoles lack teeth on the mandibles. They metamorphose, in a period ranging from as little as 20 to as much as 70 days, into tiny frogs. This sort of life history is fairly typical of most microhylids but not of all of them. Some species lack the prolonged free-swimming tadpole stage; either the egg hatches as an advanced-staged tadpole or metamorphosis is completed within the egg and a tiny froglet hatches out. This is so, for example, with *Breviceps pentheri*, of British West Africa. In this species the eggs are laid in holes on land and there is no free larval stage at all; the developing embryo lacks many of the typical tadpole structures. The tail is quite large and is presumably used as a respiratory structure, as it is in the genus *Eleutherodactylus*. The extreme microhylid life history is shown by the genus *Hoplophryne* of East Africa. *Hoplophryne uluguruensis* lays its eggs between the leaves of wild bananas or within the nodes of the stems of bamboos which have been split sufficiently to permit the entrance of this small and exceedingly depressed frog. Small amounts of water are retained in the leaves of wild bananas, but its presence has not been determined for the internodal chambers of the bamboos. The eggs hatch into tadpoles which have become specialized, as is the case in certain hylids, for existence in these rather barren environments. They have apparently taken up the habit of eating frog eggs, perhaps of their own species, and the tadpoles are consequently modified. Superficially these modifications remind one of those found, for example, in *Hyla brunnca*. The teeth are reduced to the point of being entirely absent, and the tail, like that of *Hyla brunnea*, is long, slender, and whiplike. These modifications are, of course, apparently secondary and in no sense imply close relationship.

"*Phrynomeridae* — Apparently the African toads deposit their eggs in open water. The eggs hatch out into tadpoles which later metamorphose much as do most microhylids."

The second subclass of amphibians, *Lepospondyli,* has 5 orders of which the first three became extinct. The two orders with living descendants are the *Urodela* (salamanders with 8 or more families) and *Apoda* (worm-like amphibians of a single circumtropical family, *Caeciliidae*).

The reproduction of the families of the order, *Urodela,* has been described by Goin as follows:

"Hynobiidae — The hynobiids, primitive salamanders of the Old World, practice external fertilization, and the females deposit the eggs in egg cases. *Batrachuperus karlschmidti,* a common salamander of the small mountain streams of western China, attaches its egg cases in the stream bed proper, under or on the sides of large stones in flowing water. These cases are mostly found in small brooks, especially near their source, where spring water seeps out of the ground or from under stones. The end of the egg case that is attached to the stone is flat and sticky and the body of the case is a cylindrical tube, larger in the middle and smaller toward the free end where it is smooth and transparent. The free end is covered with a smooth, cup-like cap which is even more delicate than the rest of the case. This cap is forced off by the movement of the fully developed embryos, and the young free themselves through the hole. The individual egg cases contain 7 to 12 eggs or developing embryos, and since as many as 45 eggs in the same stage of development have been taken from a single mature female, it follows that each female deposits 5 or 6 separate egg cases. The larvae are fairly typical salamander stream larvae.

Cryptobranchidae—The Salamanders of this family, like those in the family Hynobiidae, practice external fertilization. In *Cryptobranchus,* the hellbender of the eastern United States, mating takes place in the late summer. The male excavates a nest on the stream bottom beneath some large sheltering object, usually a flat rock, and will accept females that have not deposited their eggs. The eggs are laid in long rosarylike strings, one from each oviduct. These strings settle in a tangled mass on the bottom of the nest. As many as 450 eggs may be deposited by a single female, and several females may lay in a single nest. Fertilization is accomplished by the male discharging into the water a whitish, cloudy mass, consisting of seminal fluid and secretions of the cloacal glands, as the eggs are deposited by the female. After the eggs are deposited and fertilized, the male often lies among them with his head guarding the opening of the nest. It takes about 10 to 12 weeks for the eggs to hatch; the larvae transform at approximately 18 months.

"*Ambystomatidae* — In the family of the mole salamanders, two modifications not present in the previously mentioned families of salamanders show up: one is internal fertilization and the other is deposition of eggs on land. All the Ambystomatidae practice internal fertilization by means of spermatophores. These spermatophores are little packets of sperm, enclosed in a mushroom-shaped, gelatinous mass, which are deposited by the male and picked up by the cloacal lips of the female. Most of the ambystomatids, such as *Ambystoma tigrinum, A. maculatum,* and *A. jeffersonianium,* lay their eggs in water. In the last-named species, for example, the adults migrate to the breeding ponds in the early spring. The females usually outnumber the males and often must bid for attention during the mating season. After a characteristic courtship, the female picks up the spermatophore and deposits small eggs in cylindrical masses which contain on the average about 16 eggs. These eggs are, of course, fertilized as they pass down the oviduct. Since the female may deposit over 200 eggs, it often takes a number of masses to complete a deposition. Typically, the incubation period ranges from 30 to 45 days, and transformation, or metamorphosis, follows 2 to 4 months after hatching.

"*A. opacum* departs from this pattern to lay its eggs in the fall on land under old logs or other sheltering objects. The young, which hatch out on the advent of winter rains and make their way into the water, exhibit all the larval characteristics typical of other species of the genus.

"*Salamandridae* — The typical salamanders have developed a diversity of life-history patterns. Fertilization is internal by means of spermatophores. In the common American newt, *Diemictylus v. viridescens,* mating takes place in the spring. The eggs, numbering 200 to 375, are laid singly and usually are fastened to some aquatic object, such as a leaf or the stem of a small plant in quiet waters. Rarely they may be attached to the surface of a stone. The eggs hatch in about 20 to 35 days and the larval period usually lasts until fall.

"On the other hand, some species of the Old World genus *Salamandra* exhibit modified life histories. *Salamandra atra,* for example, retains the eggs in the oviduct for the developmental period, and the young are born as fully metamorphosed individuals. In *S. salamandra* the developing individuals are retained in the oviduct for a time, but they may be born as late larvae, rather than as completely metamorphosed individuals. If the larvae of these two species are dissected from the oviduct, they are found to have a long filamentous gills and rudimentary balancers that are characteristic of pond larvae. This shows that in *Salamandra* the retention of the developing young in the oviducts is a modification of the aquatic form of life history.

"*Amphiumidae* — While details of the congo eel's life history remain to be discovered, the broad picture is evident. Fertilization is apparently internal and the eggs are laid in long, rosarylike strings in shallow depressions on land beneath old logs or boards. These strings contain, in some cases, at least 150 eggs. The normally aquatic female remains with the eggs and guards them during their developmental period.

"*Plethodontidae* — Members of this specialized family of salamanders also show some specialized life histories. Hence, not one but several accounts are needed to typify the breeding habits of this family. In all the species, fertilization is internal by means of spermato-phores, but from this point on, there are modifications tending toward terrestrial adaptation. In the red sala-manders, *Pseudotriton*, the eggs are deposited in small groups hanging from tiny rootlets and other sub-merged structures in cool, muddy springs. The female stays with the eggs, but apparently when they have hatched the larvae range for themselves. The dusky salamander, *Desmognathus fuscus*, on the other hand, lays its eggs not in the water but on land. They are deposited in small, grapelike clusters in shallow ex-cavations in the soft earth, among bits of sphagnum, or underneath stones or logs. These excavations gen-erally are within a few feet of water. Upon hatching the young salamanders do not go at once to the water, but remain for a week or two on land and show definite terrestrial adaptations. The posterior limbs are longer in proportion to the trunk region than at any time dur-ing later development. Likewise the tail lacks a fin. In short, this young salamander is not merely a little larva which has not yet had a chance to reach the water but is basically a terrestrial salamander, able to move about in the damp crannies and crevices leading from the nest to the nearest pool or stream. After about 2 weeks these young terrestrial larvae take up an aquatic existence until such time as metamorphosis occurs, which it usually does when they are about 7 to 9 months of age. *Plethodon cinereus*, the red-backed sala-mander of the eastern United States, exemplifies the typical terrestrial plethodontid life history. The female lays 3 to 12 large unpigmented eggs in crannies and holes in rotten logs. Each egg adheres firmly to those previously laid, so that a little mass of eggs seemingly enclosed in a single envelope is formed. The egg cluster is usually attached to the roof of the cavity. The em-bryos develop rapidly and soon exhibit well-developed external gills. These, however, are lost on hatching. The young emerge in the same form as adults and never take up an aquatic larval existence. Finally, *Hydromantes* and *Oedipus* retain the eggs in the oviducts and give birth to fully transformed young.

"*Proteidae* — This family, which includes the well-known mud puppy, *Necturus*, is somewhat isolated structurally from the other salamanders and its members never completely metamorphose. Fertilization is internal. The female of *Necturus masculosus* lays eggs singly in still water and attaches them to the undersurface of rocks, boards, or other objects, usually in water 3 to 5 feet deep and from 50 to 100 feet from shore in shallow lakes, although they have been recorded from streams. There are from 18 to 180 eggs in each clutch. They hatch after 4 or 5 weeks. In this genus there is, of course, no metamorphosis, since these salamanders are aquatic and retain their gills throughout life. The European olm *Proteus*, under some conditions, does not lay eggs but rather retains them in the oviduct where the young undergo development, finally to be born as salamanders, which are but miniature replicas of the adult. In contrast to the caecilians, there are no special modifications known of either the larvae or the oviduct to permit the change in life history.

"*Sirenidae* — The aquatic sirens have been reported time and time again to exhibit external fertilization, but these reports have been based on the fact that no one has yet demonstrated either the production of spermatophores by the male or the presence of a receptable for storing the sperm in the cloaca of the female. Nonetheless, I am not yet convinced that the Sirenidae practice external fertilization. In *Pseudobranchus*, the dwarf siren, the eggs are deposited singly on the roots of water hyacinths and are so widely scattered that often an entire afternoon's collecting will produce less than a dozen eggs. They may be spaced as much as 5 to 10 feet apart. Dissection of mature females readily demonstrates that they may have well over 100 eggs ready for deposition at one time. It seems inconceivable that such a large number of widely scattered eggs could be fertilized externally. The eggs hatch several weeks after deposition, but of course the young larvae never metamorphose because these, like *Necturus*, are aquatic forms that retain the gills. Since in both the Hynobiidae and the Cryptobranchidae, the two families of salamanders that are known to have external fertilization, the eggs are laid in clusters, either in little capsules or packages, or in rosarylike strings, it would seem that the habit of spacing the eggs at wide intervals would be unique among salamanders with external fertilization if the Sirenidae are, in fact, really salamanders — but that is another story.

"*Leiopelmidae* — These primitive frogs have internal fertilization with the "tail" (cloacal appendage) of the male acting as a copulatory structure. In the tailed frog, *Ascaphus*, the voiceless male swims about on the bottom of a flowing stream until he finds a female. He grabs her and secures a firm grip, clasping her just in front of her hind legs and humping his body so as to bring his extended cloacal appendage into position to thrust into her cloaca. The sperm is apparently transported to the female cloaca by means of this appendage. The eggs are deposited in coils of rosarylike strings which adhere to rocks at the bottom of the stream. In the cold water in which these eggs are deposited, embryonic development is slow, and transformation does not occur until the following summer. The only close relative of *Ascaphus* is *Leiopelma* of New Zealand. This frog has been reported to lay eggs on land which go through direct development, but the details of mating and method of egg deposition are unknown.

"*Pelobatidae* — As in other families, there is a good deal of variation of life histories in the burrowing toads. The reproductive pattern of the spadefoot toad, *Scaphiopus h. holbrooki*, is somewhat typical of the New World forms in that there is a speeding up of the developmental processes in correlation with the habit of breeding in temporary waters. In torrential rains and hurricanes any time of the year from early spring to late fall, males emerge from their burrows and move to temporary rain-filled pools where they call vigorously. Calling takes place both by day and by night. When the females reach the ponds, they are clasped by the males and egg deposition occurs. The toads cling to a stiff spear of grass or other piece of vegetation beneath the surface of the water and slowly crawl up the stem, in a few minutes depositing a string of about 200 eggs. The tiny eggs hatch in a fairly short period of time, depending in part on water temperature and other external factors which have yet to be determined. Under certain conditions they may hatch within a day and a half. The little tadpoles remain in the pool for a varied period of time, depending again on conditions within the drying-up pool. That local environmental conditions have their effect can be easily demonstrated. My wife and I have taken tadpoles from a drying pool in our backyard and put them on the back porch in a jar of water from the pool, leaving other tadpoles in the puddle. Those tads left in the puddle emerged just prior to the drying up of the pond, while those in the jar of water on the back porch continued to exist for several weeks afterward as untransformed tadpoles.

"On the other hand, in the Old World pelobatid *Sooglossus seychellensis* the eggs are laid on land and the tadpoles are carried about adhering to the male's back where they undergo their development. The eggs are fairly large and the larvae hatch with hind-leg rudiments present, but have neither external nor internal gills at any stage of development."

Goin described the reproductive methods of the order, *Apoda,* with a single family. *Caecilidae.*

"*Caecilidae* — Among the caecilians, internal fertilization is the rule. In the male, the cloaca (the common chamber into which the digestive and reproductive tracts empty) can be everted and serves as a copulatory structure when the cloacas of the two sexes are brought together. We find both aquatic and terrestrial caecilians and their life histories reflect these differences. In *Ichthyophis,* a native of Ceylon, breeding takes place in spring. A burrow is prepared by the female in moist ground close to running water. She coils her body about the 20 or more relatively large-yolked eggs and guards them zealously during development, protecting them from predatory snakes and lizards. The eggs swell gradually until they are about double their original size. When ready to hatch, the embryo weighs approximately four times as much as did the original egg. External gills are present at first, but these are lost soon after hatching. The larvae, which are aquatic, metamorphose into burrowing, limbless adults that would drown if kept under water. The genus *Rhinatrema* of northern South America likewise has eggs that hatch out into aquatic larvae with external gills.

"On the other hand, *Gymnophis* and *Geotrypetes* retain the eggs in the oviducts and give birth to young which are replicas of the adults. The wall of the oviduct is provided with compound oil glands and the larvae subsist by literally eating the tissue of the wall with its included oil droplets."

PATTERNS OF LOCALIZED
EVOLUTION OF REPRODUCTION

Within each group of animals there was a pattern of evolution of reproduction. Beginning with oviparity some proceeded to ovoviviparity and others went on to true viviparity. Illustrations of all of these stages still exist at the present time in certain individuals.

The sharks, principally, were oviparous. The large-yolked egg and the succeeding embryo were enclosed within a loose fitting, expansible keratin casing and placed generally in sea water. The embryo required a long time to mature and the casing increased in size. Thus it must have been pervious at least to water and oxygen. Ovoviviparity was easily accomplished by retention of the egg and yolk in its case within the maternal reproductive tract until hatching when the fetus could be born alive. In others, this stage led to retention of the egg and yolk in the maternal reproductive tract with early fragmentation of the shell or to its entire deletion with the naked embryo, on its yolk-sac, free to swim in the uterine secretions upon which, after the yolk was exhausted, it subsisted, aided by many novel methods related elsewhere in this treatise. One of these was the development of a simple yolk-sac placenta.

Exactly the same series of sequences occurred in the amphibians, even to the retention of a simple yolk-sac placenta. The marine fishes usually were oviparous with the eggs fertilized in the surrounding water but among the Cyprinodonts a very unusual method of viviparity arose. This had no normal counterpart in any other group of animals. Here the eggs never left the ovary but were fertilized by male female copulation while they still were in the ovarian follicles where some of them matured to fetuses to be born alive. In some others the follicles ruptured into a common ovarian cavity where the same bizarre methods of nutrition as in the sharks were employed.

Furthermore, a study of the methods of reproduction in the invertebrates demonstrates that on land all species practice internal fertilization, either by spermatophores picked up by the female cloaca or by male female copulation. Such internal fertilization was necessary because before the egg was laid it required a keratinous water-tight casing which had to be applied by the maternal reproductive tract after fertilization. As in the early vertebrate sharks and amphibians some invertebrates evolved from oviparity to ovoviviparity and on to true viviparity. Such occurred in the walking worm, *Peripatus,* and here there may have been a simple yolk-sac placenta as took place in the vertebrate sharks and amphibians.

In the amphibians, alone, reproductive evolution extended much further and in the late amphibians the early embryo created for itself a housing blastocyst. This took place in the time between internal fertilization and the final site of implantation of the blastocyst which consisted of the embryo in its amniotic fluid-filled cavity and two gut sacs (yolk-sac and allantoic), all within the trophoblast covering.

Further investigation demonstrates that the reptiles who first received the blastocyst proceeded in its management by the same three methods exhibited by the invertebrates and the early vertebrates, sharks and amphibians, to wit: oviparity followed by ovoviviparity and finally true viviparity. This latter was achieved and presented to the marsupials with a yolk-sac placentation and beyond to the eutherian mammals with an allantoic placentation.

The oviparous reptiles went from oviparity to ovoviviparity and on to true viviparity. On the other hand, the birds (offshoots of oviparous reptiles), probably due to impracticality, never developed ovoviviparity nor viviparity.

One accurately might state that of the invertebrates on land, the sharks in water and the amphibians in water; each group evolved all theoretically possible modifications of the management of the simple yolked (anamniote) egg. The reptiles then did likewise in respect to the management of the simple yolked egg but here it was housed in the blastocyst (amniote), which had been presented to them by the advanced amphibians which invented it. At successive stages the reptiles evolved warm blooded offshoots; birds and the three groups of mammals, monotreme, marsupial and eutherian.

REPRODUCTION IN THE REPTILES

The reptiles received from the amphibians a blastocyst relatively controlled by the yolk-sac. This was the situation of several hundred million years of previous yolk sac domination of the anamniote egg.

By adding to the anamniote egg an overcovering trophoblast (housing) and surrounding the embryo in a private pool of water retained in the amniotic cavity there came about the necessity to care for waste products and for some method of oxygenation of the embryo's new habitat. These two necessities were obtained in one new unit, the allantoic sac, derived from the lower end of the gut as the yolk sac had come off of the gut higher up. The allantoic sac received waste products (in the anamniote embryo these were expelled into the environment) and also, being spread underneath the trophoblastic covering of the blastocyst, the allantois was able to secure oxygen perfused into its soon-to-be-acquired fetal blood vessels.

This magnificent invention was received from the amphibians by the reptiles who modified it with equally admirable inventive genius. The first thing they did was to increase tremendously the volume of yolk, produced along with the microscopic embryonic protoplasm in the ovary, and simultaneously to thicken the potential trophoblast covering into an oxygen-carbon dioxide pervious but more or less water impervious keratinous shell for deposition and incubation outside of the maternal body.

The keratin covered egg (in birds calcareous covered) could be deposited in a suitable place where the tropical sun or heat of fermentation (or body heat in birds) could incubate it. Now, there was the necessity of water to digest the yolk by the fetal vascularized yolk sac which extended from the gut and surrounded the yolk. This water, especially in birds, was incorporated with the egg in the form of albumin into the cavity of the shell by the maternal reproductive tract prior to the application of the shell by the shell gland. In reptiles where the egg (blastocyst) was incubated in a moist place little or no albumin was required. All animals employing the blastocyst in reproduction must have internal fertilization by male female copulation. This sturdy and adaptable blastocyst bore the same relation to the reptilian, avian and monotreme reproduction as the Model T automobile bore to the automotive industry in recent times.

Such was the blastocyst unit as was employed in all oviparous reptiles, all birds and all monotremes and all of these have survived to the present time without essential modification. Grand as the accomplishment was the reptiles were not satisfied and proceeded to the second significant modification of the blastocyst. This was the retention and maturation of the egg within the lumen of the maternal reproductive tract. At first this was mere retention of the shell covered egg until it hatched out and the fetus was born from the reproductive tract exit cloaca; ovoviviparity. Further evolution gradually dispensed with the egg shell and the blastocyst lay naked in the uterine cavity. However, at this stage the blastocyst essentially was dominated by the yolk sac whose vessels vascularized the trophoblastic covering of the blastocyst.

From this stage of yolk sac viviparity in the reptiles were evolved the marsupials. The marsupials then had a yolk sac placenta lying under more than half of the surface of the blastocyst. Now, oxygen could perfuse into the yolk sac capillaries and certainly did but it is apparent that oxygenation to the gestation sac must have been deficient in the marsupials. To overcome this deficiency, as soon as the embryo evolved into a fetus with the principal organs functional, it was expelled from the birth canal and attached by mouth to an intra-pouch nipple where it could obtain nutrition by swallowing milk and at the same time breathe oxygen in air through its nose.

This was the very complicated gift to the warm-blooded and fur-coated marsupials who managed, precariously, to employ the same method and to survive more than 200 million years to the present time.

The reptiles went on to create the third and final modification of the blastocyst. In this procedure the allantois learned how to obtain nutrition from the uterine secretions to equal its earlier acquired oxygen-obtaining ability. Thus the yolk sac was bypassed. This extremely important modifying invention created the perfect blastocyst with allantoic vascularized trophoblast which at this stage was presented to the warm-blooded and fur-coated eutherian mammals.

The first level of these mammals which probably began relatively early in the Mesozoic era, (Simpson, 1935) managed the blastocyst exactly as had the reptiles from whom they received it. That is, the blastocyst with allantoic vascularized trophoblast, remained relatively free in a segment of the linear lumen of one tube of a bicornuate uterus and subsisted upon uterine secretions (uterine milk).

This first level of such mammals was composed of many members each exploiting its own diverse ecology for survival. They all were equipped with a blastocyst whose allantoic vascularized trophoblast was able to obtain sufficient nutrition and also sufficient oxygen. Now, the allantoic vascularized trophoblast apparently had a property not present to great extent in the yolk sac vascularized trophoblast. This property was a tendency to unite with and to invade the surrounding maternal tissues. The progress and extent of this, of necessity, had to coincide with evolution of the uterine mucosa to allow invasion.

The whole history of the evolution of management of the allantoic vascularized blastocyst in the eutherian mammalian line is that of more and more allantoic trophoblast invasion of the maternal tissues until finally the blastocyst found itself buried in a new cavity in the mucus membrane decidua and outside of the lumen of the uterus.

A terminal, additional maternal evolution created the simplex uterus by combining the two shortened uterine horns into one but this could not have been practical until interstitial ovular decidual implantation had been created in association with one of the two tubes of the bicornuate uterus, as occurred in the vampire bat.

Every species of the eutherian mammalian line branched off in a family at some distinct stage in this evolutionary scheme.

In summary, the reptiles perfected the blastocyst from yolk sac fetal vessel domination to that of the allantoic vessels but in reptiles the blastocyst in every instance lay free in a segment of the linear and circular lumen of one tube of a didelphic uterus. There was no invasion, and subsistence, nutrition, oxygen and water were derived from the uterine secretions in which the blastocyst lay. Such a situation existed in the first level of the primitive eutherian mammalian line and this they had received from the reptiles that had perfected the blastocyst. The eutherian mammalian line did not have to evolve the blastocyst but its part in evolution lay entirely in how to manage the blastocyst in relation to the uterine lumen. This evolution began at about the end of the Mesozoic era and probably was completed within 10 million years so that in all eutherian mammals each has a basic mode of placentation received about 60 million years ago which has been rather faithfully followed throughout this period of time. The first level received its placentation much earlier in the Mesozoic era.

Any living eutherian mammal should be able to be related to one of eight or possibly nine stages in the evolution of the blastocyst-uterine lumen relationship. To accomplish this it is necessary to ascertain its mode of placentation.

The fate of the yolk sac in the eutherian mammals was variable. In the first two levels where the allantoic placenta was primarily diffuse the yolk sac was present but it was without yolk to digest and it never extended to the trophoblast. It occupied itself with the function of a storehouse of fluid which probably was used by the embryo-fetus to maintain fluid distention of the amniotic sac in which it lay.

However, in eutherian mammalian evolutionary levels 3, 4, 5, and 6 the yolk sac resumed a placental function in that there occurred in these gestations three consecutive placentas. The primary first placenta was non-vascularized trophoblastic (chorionic) the second placenta was a partial yolk sac vascularization of a limited portion of the trophoblast. The third and final placenta contained the definitive allantoic vascularized trophoblast. Thus, the two early placentas, the non-vascularized trophoblastic and the yolk sac placenta usually atrophied and disappeared when the allantoic placenta had become formed.

In the ultimate, final stages of evolution of the mammals (primates) the yolk sac from the very first of the gestation remained as a small sac in the exocoelom and soon atrophied to appear as a small, functionless mass between the amnion and chorion, such as occurs in the human gestation and in other simplex uterine mammals.

When the blastocyst had been perfected (to the allantoic vascularization of the trophoblast) by the reptiles, theoretically and practically, there could be no more evolution of the blastocyst itself.

When the blastocyst-uterine relationship had been perfected (to interstitial decidual allantoic blastocyst implantation) by the eutherian mammalian line, theoretically and practically, there could be no more evolution in this respect. Thus, when this final level of eutherian mammals had been achieved, some 60 million years ago, basic evolution ceased. Subsequent evolution lay only in rearrangement of the internal structures of the blastocyst to create families, genera and species.

Let it be understood that there are no teleological implications in this account. As long as the most efficient, final hemochorial relationship of fetal trophoblastic tissue to maternal decidual mucosa had not been accomplished those genetic mutations which pointed in this direction were more apt to succeed and thus allow rejection of those whose feto-maternal exchanges were less efficient. Thus, genetic mutations were more or less sporadic but constant and those that succeeded were the more efficient.

From the embryological record there appears to be a direct line of ascent of the eutherian mammals from the allantoic placental reptiles through the subungulates (lemurida cetacea,, perissodactyla, suidae), browsing artiodactyla, carnivora, insectivora, chiroptera to the simplex uterine primates. The rodents seem to be a very successful offshoot from the region of the insectivores. The rodents, like the successful sharks, marine fishes, birds and marsupials always had available plentiful food and thus their further basic evolution stopped. In all of these groups there were infinite numbers of variations to create multiple families, genera and species but the inherited basic mode of reproduction did not change although components of the amniote egg or of the blastocyst were subject to modification and rearrangement.

MARSUPIALS AND THEIR REPRODUCTION

It is here postulated that the marsupials became isolated in Australia when, if so, this continent became separated from the others, which must have occurred during the early Mesozoic era after the evolution of the marsupials but prior to that of the eutherian mammals. The marsupials, all with essentially yolk-sac vascularized placentas, had members which individually exploited all of the available ecological livelihoods, just as was done by the subsequently evolved eutherian mammals. Without competition from eutherian mammals in Australia the marsupials were free to evolve to the fullest extent including a variety of carnivores.

It is further proposed that in South America, separated more recently in the late Cretaceous period the marsupials were isolated along with the first level of eutherian mammals. Now these ungulates were herbivorous and eutherian carnivores of the third level had not yet evolved. So the marsupial carnivores were the only such in this continent. This may explain why there were fierce, saber-toothed like marsupials in South America and no place else. When the land bridge arose between South and North Americas a few million years ago, the, by then, developed eutherian mammalian carnivores in North America crossed the land bridge into South America and preyed, not only upon the primitive eutherian ungulates and the herbivorous or insectivorous marsupials, but also upon the carnivorous marsupials evolved there. In Australia there were no large four footed ungulates and the marsupial saber-toothed carnivore had no opportunity to evolve, although Romer noted that there are Australian fossils of giant herbivorous marsupials up to 11 feet long.

A somewhat similar situation may be described. When sheep first were introduced into Australia, the marsupial, carnivorous wolf, until decimated by man, had a field day with the defenseless sheep.

In Australia the marsupials prospered because there was no eutherian mammalian competition. In South America they survived because for millions of years there were no eutherian mammalian carnivores.

It appears that Australia may have separated from the other continents in the Mesozoic era after the origin of the monotremes and marsupials and before eutherian mammals evolved. Thus, the monotremes and marsupials were the only mammals there, of course in addition to reptiles and others which evolved earlier.

It also appears that South America may have separated from the other continents late in the Mesozic, but after one level of eutherian mammals had evolved. Thus, South America should have had invertebrates, early vertebrates, amphibians, reptiles, monotremes, marsupials and the primary level of eutherian mammals, but no eutherian carnivores, until the land bridge to North America was built late in the Cenozoic era. However, there were marsupial carnivores, one of which simulated the saber-toothed tiger in structure and violence.

In his classic volume on the embryology of the opossum, 1938, Edward McCrady, Jr. working at The Wistar Institute of Anatomy and Biology, Philadelphia, presented a short history of the relatively difficult studies leading to the solution of knowledge of the reproductive procedures in this hardy and mysterious mammal.

Prior to 1887 Emil Selenka imported a large number of American opossums to Erlangen, Germany. He obtained several litters of eggs and embryos before the colony became sterile and the animals died. About

1916, Carl Hartman in Texas solved almost all of the problems, using freshly caught animals which abounded in the neighborhood. In his technical details of the embryology he had for a short time the services of Chester Heuser. But the problem of maintaining a colony in captivity still persisted and no colony had been established. The animals all developed rickets, became sterile and died. This was a particular type of rickets not amenable to vitamine D. McCrady found that in the wild state the animal had eaten bones as well as lean meat and eggs. He consequently added bone meal to the diet and obtained healthy animals but ones which still did not breed well. Acting upon the suggestion of Hartman that they needed exercise McCrady placed secluded resting boxes high in a tree in the pen and he placed the food pans on the floor. Thus they were compelled to climb up to rest during the day and to climb down to eat at night. From then on the animals remained healthy and produced healthy litters. Adhering to these principles colonies readily may be maintained.

As previously noted, associated with the development of the embryology and reproduction of opossums are three prominent names, Selenka, Hartman and McCrady, whose writings encompass the field. They finally solved the mystery surrounding the subject since the first opossum was brought to Spain by the early Spanish explorers to the Americas. This unusual mammal created a scientific sensation in Europe primarily because of its young-bearing pouch. Australian marsupials were yet to be discovered.

The problem of the birth of the opossum was solved by Dr. and Mrs. Hartman before 1920. They took turns observing a female at near parturition time. The animal was in a darkened window box, lighted only by a dim red light. The infants (truly in the early fetal stage) are born through the urogenital sinus with the mother propped up in a semi-sitting position where she could tongue-moisten the tract of hair from the birth canal to the pouch. The newborn, with the use of hooked claws on digits of their front limbs, climb, hair by hair, up into the pouch which is several inches above the vulva. Here they each attach themselves by mouth to a mammary gland nipple where they remain for 50 days. Commonly there are 13 nipples. Since more than 13 may be born the latecomers die of starvation. Once in the pouch the digit claws loosen and drop off.

In most vertebrates with two linear (bicornuate) uterine channels multiple gestation sacs are distributed, fairly evenly, along the two uterine canals, but in opossums the lower ends of the two tubular uteri are expanded each into a uterus (didelphic) capable of maturation of a dozen or more fertilized eggs all in the same space. The eggs with a small amount of yolk and a larger amount of albumen enclosed in a membrane are about 1/32 inch in diameter and at the time of birth the blastocysts must be nearly a centimeter in diameter. From Hartman's description the blastocysts may be enmeshed in highly vascular folds of uterine mucosa.

At the beginning of the fetal period labor occurs and they escape from the uteri by a very complex maneuver common to all marsupials. In the reproductive anatomy of the female there is a single urogenital sinus, separate from the rectum, but the urethra opens into the apex at which point the vagina bifurcates into two lateral widely arched narrow segments which extend outward but soon swing medianward to join, on each side, a vaginal cul-de-sac underneath each uterine cervix. At parturition the uterine contractions probably rupture the blastocysts which remain behind in the uterus while the fetuses each in its own amnion sac are passed into the vaginal cul-de-sac on either side. These cul-de-sacs probably with a thin wall are ruptured in such fashion that the fetuses are expelled into the apex of the single urogenital sinus from which they pass outside of the mother's body. They thus by-pass the bifurcated upper vaginal arches.

According to Wood Jones, 1944, and based upon Hill's work, the ureters in marsupials lie inside of the Muellerian ducts. The two narrow vaginas from the apex of the urogenital sinus each extend lateralward to go around the ureter on either side and then curve backward to connect with a cul-de-sac underneath each uterine cervix. Thus the two distinct uteri never were able to join to form a monodelphic uterus and for this reason remained didelphic. Wood Jones stated "It cannot be too strongly insisted that the feature that distinguishes all marsupials from all other mammals is the fact that in them the ureters pass between the female genital ducts, whereas in all other mammals they pass lateral to them".

In the male opossum the erectile muscular penis uses the female urogenital sinus as a vagina and the penis is longitudinally split at the distal end so that one part serves each of the true vaginas.

Apparently the marsupials were a closely related group and the female genitalia were similar throughout the order. The urethra opened into the top of the lower single urogenital sinus near the site of its bifurcation into two laterally swinging vaginal arches which above turn inward each around an ureter to join a cul-de-sac under each of the two uteri. Parturition is similar throughout the order in that the fetuses in their amniotic sacs are expelled into the vaginal cul-de-sacs and from there by rupture directly into the apex of the single urogenital sinus bypassing the two bifurcated vaginal arches. The remainder of the fetal membranes, other than the amnion, are retained in the uterus to be absorbed probably by phagocytosis.

During maturation of the fertilized egg the blastocyst is formed and a large part of its cavity is filled by the yolk sac which vascularizes the trophoblast. The embryo in its amniotic cavity and its independent allantoic sac for its excretions all sink down into the yolk sac as into a pillow. The yolk sac placenta covers more than one half of the blastocyst and must absorb water, nutrition and oxygen since there is a limited quantity of yolk and the allantois remains as a closed sac, pedunculated to the embryo's abdomen. This never reaches to and consequently cannot vascularize the trophoblast. It remains filled with fetal excretions in liquid form until parturition when it is ruptured and collapses. (Bandicoots were an exception).

Since the epithelia of the uterine mucosa and of the trophoblast are not breached, the only sources of oxygen, water and nutrition are the uterine gland secretions in which the blastocyst is bathed and all must be acquired for the embryo by the yolk sac placenta.

If as generally conceded mammals evolved from reptiles, then the most likely group of reptiles from which the marsupials came should be those which had evolved further than ovoviviparity and beyond to a yolk sac placenta with elimination of the allantois for any purpose than to retain fetal excretions. There are thousands of living reptile species not yet investigated as to reproduction but of those score or more of viviparous reptiles whose reproductive methods are known all still retain, in addition to the yolk sac placenta some degree of allantoic trophoblast attachment.

If all viviparous reptilian reproductive processes had been studied, no doubt there would be found a few in existence with yolk-sac placenta and with complete abeyance of the allontoic placenta with the allantoic sac retained solely as a receptacle for fetal wastes as occurs in most marsupials. The only exception is in *Perameles,* but this is considered to be an example of not primitive but of advanced evolution.

Among the score or more of viviparous reptiles (including a family of snakes) so far investigated as to reproduction, those with a yolk sac placenta approaching that of the opossum still possess an accessory allantoic placental portion. This, in most marsupials, was completely suppressed with dependence entirely upon the yolk sac placenta.

If the Grosser classification were applied here, most viviparous reptiles and most marsupials would be classed epitheliochorial. A few in each of the two groups may approach the status of syndesmochorial. Thus for the most part the fetal vascularized trophoblast acquires oxygen, water and nutrition from uterine gland secretions or more directly from uterine mucosal syncytial cell exudations.

In the viviparous anamniote vertebrates from the sharks to and including almost all amphibians the independent yolk sac had a long history of acquiring these same three substances in more or less the same fashion, although the great store of ovary deposited yolk was the main primitive source.

There is little doubt that oxygen in high concentration will perfuse into exposed yolk sac vessels but the allantois may have acquired the ability to obtain oxygen at low tension. This function the yolk sac endoderm appears never to have reached. Consequently, the marsupials (with the exception of *Perameles*) were equipped only with a yolk sac placenta. The oxygenation function appeared to be adequate enough only to develop the embryo into a fetus but not enough to supply the rapidly growing fetus to term. The only way out of the dilemma, other than extinction, was early delivery of the fetus to be cared for in another supplementary fashion, i.e. attachment of the fetus by mouth to a mammary gland nipple for further development to term. Complex as were the methods of parturition and of nutrition of the embryo-fetus-newborn, the marsupials survived to the present time in certain parts of the earth, a period of possibly 200 million years.

PLACENTATION OF THE KANGAROO RAT

Following about six years of part time study T. T. Flynn, Professor of Biology, University of Tasmania, in 1930 described the reproduction in the kangaroo rat, *Bettongia cuniculus,* a small, rare, diprotodont marsupial found is Tasmania. His summary in part follows. "The breeding season of *Bettongia* is known with certainty to extend over ten months of the year, from the beginning of March to the third week in December. *Bettongia* is polyestrous. Ovulation is spontaneous and unilateral, one ovum being discharged at each ovulation. Each ovary supplies its own uterus. Pregnancy is unilateral and under normal conditions occurs alternately in each uterus. Gestation and lactation periods each are of about six weeks duration. When breeding is active, the gestation and lactation periods overlap, i.e. a new pregnancy may occur while there is still present a pouch fetus." Flynn stated.

"While one uterus is pregnant the contralateral one enters into and remains in a condition of pseudo-pregnancy which persists till parturition, probably due to the hormones supplying the pregnant uterus.

"In pregnancy embryotrophic material is present in abundance and consists mainly of a transudate from the epithelium with included epithelial cells, cellular debris, leucocytes and haematids.

"The amnion arises by folds, of which the head fold appears first. The allantois remains small and no allanto-chorion is formed. As effectual placenta is developed by the close opposition of the (yolk sac vascularized) trophoblast to the uterine epithelium. Actual union without penetration occurs, being most marked and appearing first in the region of the vascular omphalopleure.

"Parturition occurs when the embryo measures about 14.5 mm in direct length. The foetal membranes are retained in the uterus and are absorbed with the aid of maternal leucocytes."

Flynn did not describe the maternal reproductive anatomy nor the process of parturition but these probably were very similar to those in the opossum.

EARLY EMBRYOLOGY OF DIDELPHYS AURITA

Hill collected material in Brazil in 1913. This marsupial, probably opossum-like, is locally named Gamba. The expedition arrived by chance in the breeding season and 46 specimens were obtained. Eight were pregnant females and 19 had pouch young. Three were non-pregnant females and 16 were males. Pouch and reproductive tract apparently are similar to those of *Didelphys virginiana*, with two similar uteri, side by side, each of which may have ten or more fertilized eggs or embryos. The right uterus usually has one or more than the left. The specimens produce fertilized eggs in the uteri in the process of maturation and in subsequent stages up to about twenty cell blastocysts.

Neither the placenta nor parturition were described but it may be assumed that they were similar to those of the North American opossum.

In the same region in Brazil were several pouchless marsupials, small rat-like forms in the genera *Marmosa* and *Peramys*. These were shy and retiring and were difficult to secure in numbers.

PLACENTATION IN PARAMELES

Hill, in 1897-98, skillfully described gestation in Bandicoots, (*Perameles*). As in all marsupials there are two distinct uteri each of which may house one or more embryos. The uterine mucosa markedly hypertrophies and cell membranes become lost forming a syncytium through which ramify maternal capilliaries. In the blastocyst there is a discoidal area of fusion of the allantois with the trophoblast. The fetal ectoderm, when attachment is complete, consists of a single layer of greatly enlarged cells roughly cuboidal or columnar in shape. Their irregular outer ends accurately fit into the irregularities of the surface of the syncytium and are firmly adherent.

Surrounding the margin of the discoid allantoic placental area is a wide band of yolk sac vascularized trophoblast, creating an annular zone on the blastocyst. Here the maternal syncytium is more highly vascularized than that over the allantoic placenta. Hill considered that this yolk sac placental area was in the process of degeneration as the allantoic placentation advanced in function. This was demonstrated by the fact that the vitelline vein is three times as large as the allantoic vein.

Parturition occurs by the unique method common to all marsupials and the placenta does not loosen from the uterine mucosa but remains to be absorbed. Although limited in numbers to two or three, the new born infants of *perameles* appear to be similar to and no further developed than those of the opossum. Since they possess tiny hooks on the digits of the arms the mode of climbing into the pouch must be the same.

Fate dealt the marsupials a double dose of adversity, (1) an extremely complicated maternal reproductive tract which must have occurred in some unknown reptilian ancestor but no where else in the animal kingdom, and (2) a primitive yolk-sac placenta deficient in ability to acquire oxygen for more than the development of the embryo which, as soon as it became a fetus, was expelled for further maturation in a mammary pouch. In spite of these defects, enough to warrant extinction, the marsupials never gave up but

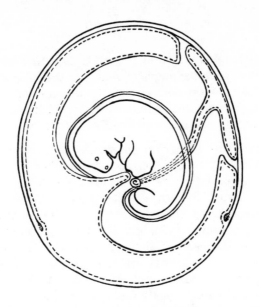

Fig. 7.—The placentation of the marsupial Perameles. Most of the trophoblast is vascularized by the underlying yolk-sac vessels but there also is an accessory allantoic placenta. Redrawn from J. P. Hill, Quart. J. Micro. Sci. 40: 385-446, 1897-98.

managed to survive for approximately 250 million years and in many localities in competition with the superior intelligence of the allanto-placental eutherian mammals whose fetuses were well supplied with oxygen and thus could remain in the uterus for complete development.

CHIROPTERA AND THEIR PLACENTATION

E. P. Walker, a long time student of bats, in his *Mammals of the World,* 1968, published more than 200 illustrations of individual bats and a summary of each. The order Chiroptera has been classified into two suborders; Megachiroptera and Microchiroptera. The Megachiroptera has a single family, Pteropodidae. The Microchiroptera has 16 families.

While the embryology of the Pteropodidae is similar to that of some of the more evolved members of the Microchiroptera, these bats possess distinct appearance. The Pteropodidae, being fruit-eating bats, depend more upon vision and smell to find food and they lack the nose appendages of many of the insectivorous bats. They possess pointed muzzles and appear fox-like. Thus, they have been given a common name of flying foxes, some with a wingspread of 5 feet.

Among the eutherian mammals only the rodents exceed the bats (178 genera) in number of species. With the exception of the usually clawed thumb the four extended fingers act like umbrella ribs to support the skin extensions from the sides of the body and tail. In some there may be an interfemoral skin sheath at the rear of the body and the tail may extend beyond the center of the margin (free-tailed) or it may be entirely enclosed in the sheath (sheath-tailed). Likewise, the Microchiroptera being principally insect eaters often possess varying types of nose excrescences, probably sensory organs used in echolocation. Possibly the tragus in the external ear of the Microchiroptera also serves as a sense organ. Bats, being fur-coated and of high metabolism may maintain high body temperature which usually is reduced to near that of the environment when resting or sleeping. Hanging head down probably aids in oxygenation of the central nervous system. Some bats have a degree of fusion of certain vertebrae.

Most bats have only one young per year but this may be offset by a long life. In hibernating forms ovulation occurs in the spring with breeding generally taking place in the previous fall. In the interval the sperms are retained in the female reproductive tract (delayed insemination). Female bats usually have one pair of functional mammary glands located in the chest region. In the male the testes descend into a temporary sac during the breeding season. The penis has a primate-like appearance.

Most of the Microchiroptera are insectivorous, catching flying insects in darkness by echolocation.

Some, however, are additionally fruit eaters and some are carnivorous with a diet of small animals or of top minnows caught by powerful, clawed feet while flying near the surface of the water. The Microchiropteran Desmodus, is a true vampire living entirely upon blood, generally of large animals.

Walker described the bats under the following families.

Suborder Megachiroptera.

Pteropodidae — 39 genera and approximately 130 species. Generally fruit eaters who depend somewhat on good vision.

Suborder Microchiroptera.

Rhinopomatidae — A single genus with 4 species. Insectivorous.

Emballonuridae — 13 genera and 40 species. Insectivorous.

Noctilionidae — A single genus with 2 species: *N. leporinus* has a pointed muzzle and lacks nose excrescenses. It feeds on small fish which it catches with clawed feet, free of membranes. The other of the 2 species, *N. labialis* feeds on insects.

Nycteridae — A single genus and about 10 species; generally insectivorous.

Megadermatidae. 3 genera and 5 species, generally insectivorous.

Rhinolophidae — 2 genera with complex nose-leaf, generally insectivorous.

Hipposideridae — 9 genera and 40 species, with nose-leaf, and generally insectivorous. They occasionally have two newborn.

Phyllostomidae — 51 genera and approximately 140 species. Tropical and subtropical. Range from small to largest of American bats. Nose-leaf reduced or absent. In the external ear a tragus is present. In subfamily *Glossophaginae*, the snout is elongate and the tongue is long. They feed on nectar, pollen, fruit juices and insects. The development in this family parallels that of the Old World fruit bats, *Pteropodidae*. The *Phyllostomidae* are the only bats to make a shelter, which they do by biting through the main rib of a large leaf so that the distal portion bends down.

Desmodontidae — A single species, rotundus, in the South American vampire bat. Gestation period 90-120 days. The young are not carried by the mother. Life-span, 12 years.

Natalidae — A single genus, without leaf-nose. Insectivorous.

Furipteridae — 2 genera and 2 species, related to *Vespertilionidae*, Insectivorous.

Thyropteridae — A single genus and related to *Vespertilionidae*.

Vespertilionidae — 38 genera and 275 species. Insectivorous.

Molossidae — 10 genera and possibly 80 species, 'free-tailed'. Nose-leaf absent but horn-like projections may be present. Diet, insects, often hard-shelled forms. Carlbad Cave bats. — Two species (*Cheiromeles*) are hairless. Diet, large insects.

In fairly early stages in the history of embryology in the latter part of the past century, vespertilionid bats must have been plentiful, easily located and easily secured at any season of the year in France. They thus became the principal object of study of mammalian gestation and several monographs were published devoted mainly to the development and understanding of the mammalian embryo and its blastocystic membranes, the yolk sac, the amnion, the allantois and the trophoblast. Other common domestic animals, rabbits, pigs and sheep also were used but this particular bat furnished the most complete and voluminous investigations.

van Beneden, 1888-99, reported his studies of more than 300 gestation sacs secured at various stages. Duval, 1895, produced a similar extensive study.

Zoologists have grouped all bats into one order of mammals. There is one superfamily of large sized bats, Megachiroptera, (pteropus) and 16 families of small sized bats, Microchiroptera, into four superfamilies Emballonuroidea, Rhinolophoidea, Phyllostomatoidea, and Vespertilionoidae. Slightly more than half of the families have been involved in studies of the reproductive processes and an insignificant per cent of the species.

Sansom, 1932, studied the blastocysts of five individuals of *Molossus rufus* or *M. obscurus*. All five blastocysts were central in one tube of a bicornuate uterus.

Stephens, 1962, reported upon placentation in 126 free-tailed bats, *Tadarida cynocephala* (Molossidae). These were captured near Gainesville, Florida. At term the fetus weighs nearly one fourth as much as the mother and usually is born from breech presentation. Almost all gestations occur in the right uterine horn and from ovulation of the right ovary. In elaboration of the blastocyst the yolk-sac first develops almost filling the blastocyst and although the yolk-sac atrophies during gestation a small part continues to be attached to the tropoblast. The amnion sac is accomplished by folding. The allantois develops early. At first it is a diverticulum of the yolk sac and only secondarily from the hindgut. It reaches its greatest size during the limb-bud stage. The stalk and cavity disappear before mid gestation but its vessels completely vascularize the chorion as well as the attached tip of the yolk sac.

In implantation the blastocyst lies free in the lumen

of the (usually) right horn of the uterus. The blastocyst enlarges and makes contact with the wall of the uterine cavity on all sides (central implantation). The covering syncytial trophoblast breaks down the uterine epithelium and then continues to cytolize the endometrium and connective tissue surrounding the maternal capillary bed. Thus is formed a diffuse, labyrinthine, syndesmochorial placenta. This is short lived and is changed to endotheliochorial. The diffuse, labyrinthine, endotheliochorial allantoic placenta gradually is restricted to one area on the blastocyst.

Comment. Central implantation of the blastocyst with development of a diffuse, allantoic, endotheliochorial placenta later to be restricted to a girdle area or to two discs or to one disc seems to place the molossid bat in the carnivore line. This concept is supported by the presence of what amounts to a hematoma, common to the carnivores.

Scrivastava, 1952, studied placentas in several stages of gestation in *Rhinopoma kinneari*. He showed that there is an early non-vascular yolk-sac placenta followed by a vascularized yolk-sac placenta. These are superseded by the definitive allantoic placenta. The blastocyst lies centrally in one tube of a bicornuate tubular uterus and the lamelliform attachment becomes endotheliochorial. This diffuse placenta later is restricted to a discoid area on the mesometrial side. The placenta, finally, is saucer-like with an irregular margin and it tends to split into 2 unequal halves, "The nature of the placental labyrinth is lamellar, much like that of the carnivores". There is no hematoma but the yolk sac placenta persists to term and is transformed into a gland providing internal secretion.

Comment: This bat seems to have placentation more similar to that of the carnivores than of that of any other group.

Gopalakrishna, 1958, reported upon three species of

bats collected in the early part of the year from regions in Central and North India. These species were *Taphozous longimanus*, (Emballonuridae) 58 gravid uteri; *Rhinopoma kinneari*, (Rhinopomidae) 18 pregnant uteri, and *Hipposideros bicolor pallidus*, (Hipposideridae), 24 pregnant uteri.

In each of these three species the blastocyst filled the lumen of a segment of usually the right tube of a bicornuate tubular uterus. The primary placenta was diffuse with yolk-sac vascularized trophoblast. This diffuse yolk-sac placenta was replaced by allantoic vascularization. The diffuse allantoic placenta, centrally situated, then became restricted to one area on the blastocyst. The general features are such that they fall into the carnivore line of placentation. Furthermore the author described a hematoma in association with the definitive placenta especially in *Taphozous longimanus*. The yolk-sac degenerates into possibly a gland structure.

Wimsatt and Gopalakrishna, 1958, discussed the hematoma of the Emballonurid bats found in India and in Central America. They stated that this is the most primitive family of the Microchiroptera. In six genera the hematoma structure was present in five and in the other the gestation was too immature to determine its presence. Thus it may be common to all members of this family of bats. The authors described in detail the hematomas which usually are single, forming a sac-like structure at the margin of the placenta and near the generally mesometrial insertion of the umbilical cord. The hematoma appeared to be part of the placenta but of markedly different internal morphology. Here, where it attaches to its area of endometrium the trophoblast, in the form of lamellae and villi, attacks the endometrium much more extensively, eroding into the endometrial blood vessels and allowing maternal blood to infiltrate the center of the hematoma sac where it is processed by the trophoblast for the benefit (iron or otherwise) of the fetus.

Wimsatt, 1944, reported a study of all stages of ovular implantation in the vespertilionid bat, *Myotis lucifugus lucifugus*. The uterus with its two horns, together measure about 3 or 4 mm. The cross section of the implantation cavity in one of the two horns, usually the right, reveals that the lumen is roughly elliptical with the greatest diameter mesometrial and antimesometrial. The mucosa at the antimesometrial end of the cross section is much thicker than is that near the mesometrium. He described the progestation changes in the endometrium especially at this site where implantation occurs. The blastocyst first establishes contact with the endometrium at the antimesometrial side of the lumen and orientation of the embryonic disc also is antimesometrial. Although the blastocyst is in contact with the wall of the uterus on all sides of the implantation cavity, the placenta develops only at the antimesometrial side and its definitive discoidal appearance continued from the first attachment. Further penetration of the blastocyst does not occur and there is no consequent decidua capsularis.

For many years many bats have been reported to be, and generally assumed to be, hemochorial. However, in 1958 Wimsatt reported upon a comprehensive investigation, reviewing 23 species in respect to this point. Using many differential tissue stains and refined optical methods, he was able to demonstrate at least an interstitial membrane barrier between the fetal and maternal blood streams. This interstitial membrane may be so thin that it has escaped notice of all but a few previous observers and even then it may have been misinterpreted.

In all 23 species of bats studied none was considered to be hemochorial excepting Molossidae in the later stages of gestation.

Gopalakrishna, 1949, from study of a large number of gestation sacs described ovular implantation in the vespertilionid bat, *Scotophilus wroughtoni*. The early blastocyst lying free in the uterine lumen undergoes enlargement and fills the local segment of the tubular uterine lumen. Changes occur in the uterine endometrial wall at the antimesometrial site of implantation, even before the embryo touches it. The blastocyst remains central while the blastocyst at the embryonic polar region attaches so that the resulting placenta is primarily discoid, antimetrial and endotheliochorial. The yolk sac is large, causing the blastocyst to fill most of the segment of the tubular uterine lumen and as the embryo and distended amniotic sac enlarge, it begins to collapse. As the amnion presses the embryonic half of the yolk sac invaginated into the abembryonic half there is produced an incomplete inverted yolk sac. At an early stage both choriovitelline and chorioallantoic placentas are functional but later the yolk-sac loses all of its placental significance and is completely replaced by the allantoic placenta. The author thoroughly discussed the formation of the amnionic cavity which is by cavitation.

Comment: It appears that the ovular implantation in the vespertilionid bat, with its blastocyst central in the uterine lumen and with only a localized area implanting in an endotheliochorial fashion to produce a primarily discoid placenta is similar to that of the rabbit or of tarsius.

Moghe, 1951, reported studies of placentation in the Indian fruit bat, *Pteropus giganteus giganteus,* in 100 gestations collected over a period of time of nearly ten years.

The ovary is situated at the anterior end of the oviduct and is enclosed in a complete ovarian capsule. The fallopian tube arises from the face of the ovary within the capsule, runs over the inner side of the ovary and

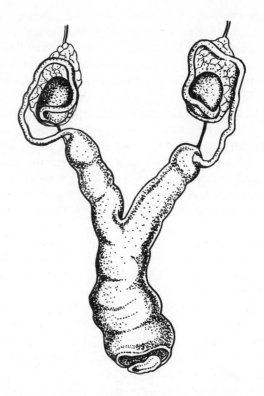

Fig. 8.—Uterus, fallopian tubes and ovaries of Indian fruit bat
Pteropus giganteus giganteus. Redrawn from Moghe. Proc. Zool.
Soc. London. 121: 703-721, 1951. Permission from Zool. Soc. London.

then lies anterior to it and finally on the outer lateral
side of the ovary. It is not much coiled but forms one
loop towards the base of the ovary whence it passes
into the uterus. Pregnancy occurs in either the right
or left horn but never in both at the same time. The
uterus is bicornuate and each horn is about a cm long.
The conjoined uterus has a dividing septum to near
the vaginal opening. The uterine lumen on each side
is elongated dorsoventrally.

Ovular-decidual implantation is illustrated in (fig.
9). The trophoblast on one side of the blastocyst lies
in close apposition to a special knob of endometrium

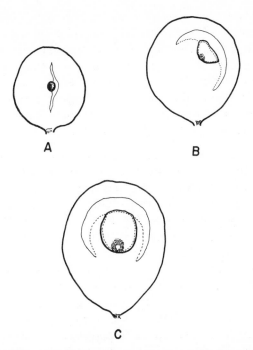

A

B

C

Fig. 9.—Blastocyst implantation and placental development in
Pteropus giganteus giganteus. Note that the placenta becomes mesometrial in site. Redrawn from Moghe, Proc. Zool. Soc. London. 121:
703-721, 1951. Permission from Zool. Soc. London.

and the uterine epithelium is lost. The trophoblast invades the endometrium. The embryonic knob is a mass
of uterine tissue protruding into the lumen of the
uterus and is attached to the myometrial layers of the
uterus towards the mesometrium.

This placenta is non-vascular yolk sac type, bilaminar
omphalopleure. Mesodermal cells extend into the bilaminar omphalopleure converting it into a trilaminar
structure except for a small region of yolk sac wall
towards the abembryonic pole. This persists to term.
The vascularized placenta may now be designated
choriovitelline. During the embryonic limbbud stage
the allantoic stalk is formed. Its mesodermic vessels
progressively penetrate the trophoblast. The placenta

on this side then becomes allantochorionic. The whole of the protruding endometrial knob becomes converted into placenta. Extension of the chorioallantoic placenta now converts the yolk sac placenta into chorioallantoic placenta. In its final form the placenta is disc shaped on the mesometrial side. The placenta, therefore, is mesometrial, discoidal, labyrinthine and haemachorial. The amnion was formed by cavitation.

Comment: Among mammals there are others which appear to possess a similar type of placentation in that the blastocyst erodes half way into the endometrium (decidua). One is the armadillo where the blastocyst has only a limited site for implantation at the very apex of a simplex uterine canal. The other is the baboon where the flattened blastocyst burrows half of its surface into one triangular sheet of decidua in a simplex uterus with a slit-like cavity. The macaque may do the same, but it usually also attaches to the opposite decidual sheet and thereby develops a duplex placenta (one disc on each opposing decidual face). There is no record of this happening in the baboon although it theoretically is possible.

Apparently the megachiropteran *Pteropus* was in the process of developing a blastocyst, interstitial, decidual type of implantation. However the intrauterine site was mesometrial while future evolution seemed to favor the antimesometrial site of implantation. This evolution appears to have been left to the insectivorous microchiroptera who, in general, had the definitive allantoic placenta antimesometrial in intrauterine site.

Anderson and Wimsatt, 1963, reported a study of 70 uteri and gestation sacs of *Noctilio labialis minor* from Panama with the breeding season assumed to be late in November or in December. The uterus (fig. 10) apparently similar to that of *Desmodus rotundus,* is composed of a short body with two equal, stubby horns.

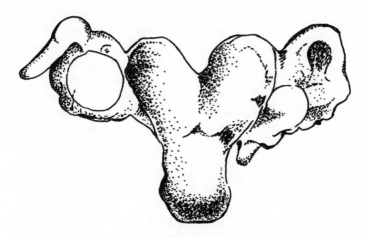

Fig. 10.—Uterus, fallopian tubes and ovaries of a Central American noctilionid bat, Noctilio labialis minor. Note the short and stubby uterine horns. Redrawn from Anderson and Wimsatt, Am. J. Anat. 112: 181-201, 1963.

The body has a septum but the cervix is single. From the apex of each horn arises a tortuous oviduct extending upwards to the ovarian bursae on each side. The bursae have openings into the peritoneal cavity.

A striking feature is a ridge of endometrium, lateral to antimesometrial, running the length of each uterine horn. The decidual reaction seems to be confined mainly to this buldging ridge which appears to have a median sulcus into which the earliest blastocyst implants.

The amnion is considered to arise from cavitation rather than by folding. The allantoic cavity is small but the allantoic mesoderm including the vessels occupies a large part of the exocoelom. In later stages the allantois is represented by a narrow duct in the umbilical cord. The yolk-sac placentation is characterized by three stages. At implantation the yolk sac apparently herniates out of the decidual crypt and thus the bilaminar omphalopleure is in contact with the decidua parietalis surrounding the lumen of the tubular uterus.

There is a prominent Reichert's membrane intervening between the inner vitelline layer and the outer trophoblastic layer of the omphalopleure. The large yolk sac, full of fluid, is pressed upon by the growing embryo in its distended amniotic sac and is eventually compressed so that its embryonic half is joined with the abembryonic half already joined to the trophoblast in that area. Thus there is tendency to yolk sac inversion. The blastocyst then becomes central in the lumen of one tube of the bicornuate uterus with the primarily discoid placenta attached to decidua basalis but without decidua capsularis.

After possibly six different placental areas in various stages (chorioamniotic, several stages of choriovitelline and later all superseded by the chorioallantoic) the definitive chorioallantoic placenta is more or less discoid, lateral to antimesometrial, with the blastocyst central. It is labyrinthine endotheliochorial.

Comment: The overall picture in this bat is somewhat similar to that in some insectivores which possess an antimesometrial crytic decidual implantation. An early ovular attachment is by yolk sac. In some of these the enlarging blastocyst herniates out of the crypt. In others the yolk-sac placenta in the bottom of the decidual crypt becomes the site of the subsequent definitive allantoic placenta which obliterates it and the blastocyst persists surrounded by decidua in the crypt.

In 1954 Wimsatt described placentation in the vampire bat *Desmodus rotundus murinus*. This bicornuate uterine bat is similar in placentation to the phyllostomid bats with a simplex uterus. The uterus (fig. 11) is bicornuate and both horns are equal in size; the single pregnancy may occur in either horn. The fallopian tubes arise from the apex of the horns and are coiled upwards to the ovary on each side. The ovum segments rapidly and loses its zona pellucida while still in the oviduct. The trophoblast probably thickens over the

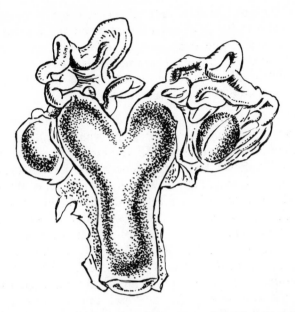

Fig. 11.—Uterus, fallopian tubes and ovaries of the bat Desmodus rotundus. Note the shape of the uterus. The Desmodontidae compose the family of bats believed to be most closely related to the simplex uterine Phyllostomidae. Redrawn from Wimsatt, Acta Anatomica, 41: 285-341, 1954. Permission of author and Swets & Zeitlinger, B.V.

embryonic pole and the implantation is of the burrowing, cytolytic type. The specimens clearly reveal that in *Desmodus rotundus* the implantation is cytolytic and completely interstitial, similar to the phyllostomid bats described by Hamlett, 1935, and by Wislocki and Fawcett, 1941. *D. rotundus* has a bicornuate uterus while the two phyllostomid bats described have simplex uteri. The uterus of *D. rotundus* is closer in anatomy to the simplex type than that of any other bat excepting the two described.

The blastocyst yolk-sac fills and distends the blastocyst and its endothelial wall joins and fuses with the trophoblast but does not vascularize it. Thus when the embryo and amniotic sac enlarge, the latter presses upon the embryonic surface of the yolk-sac. This surface is then pressed outward and is invaginated into the abembryonic half of the yolk-sac (incomplete inversion). Its total detachment from the trophoblast never occurs and it apparently does not form a gland presumably of internal secretion as in several other bats. The allantois is rudimentary but its fetal blood vessels vascularize the trophoblast.

Comment: In the course of my studies in respect to mammalian placentation it was postulated that ovular-decidual interstitial implantation must have been developed first in a more primitive bicornuate uterus. Subsequently it was discovered that Wimsatt 1954, had almost perfectly described this situation in the bat *Desmodus rotundus*. This appears to be the first mammal with completely interstitial ovular decidual implantation in a single tube of a bicornuate tubular uterus. The African bush baby, *Galago demidoffi*, is the only other mammal with a bicornuate uterus and interstitial decidual implantation of the blastocyst in the antisometrial wall of one of the two horns.

I also discovered that Moghe, 1951, previously had reported a ten year study of megachiropter *Pteropus giganteus giganteus*. This mammal has a bicornuate uterus similar to *D. rotundus* (fig. 11) and an interstitial ovular decidual implantation but only about half of the blastocyst (area increased in later gestation) invades the decidua. This partial interstitial implantation is mesometrial but otherwise similar to that of armadillos and of baboons. These mammals each possess a simplex uterus.

Hamlett, 1935, studied 23 gestation sacs of the phyllostomid bat, *Glossophaga soricina soricina*. The uterus *is completely simplex* (fig. 12) and seems to be characteristic of all phyllostomid bats. The uterine ends of the fallopian tubes lie almost parallel to each other and enter the uterus cranially instead of laterally.

The blastocystic trophoblast thickens at the embry-

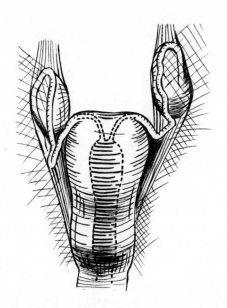

Fig. 12.—Uterus, fallopian tubes and ovaries of a Phyllostomid bat, Glossophaga soricina soricina. Redrawn from Hamlett, Am. J. Anat. 56: 327-344, 1935.

onic pole prior to implanting by erosion into the apical uterine endometrium where the blastocyst buries itself and the surface mucosa closes over the opening. Thus, there is decidua basalis and a complete decidua capsularis as in the human implantation. The latter remains presumably to term but does not grow into the decidua vera on the opposite wall of the simplex uterus where this decidua vera maintains its epithelial covering intact. The amnion is formed by cavitation. When first developed the yolk-sac soon almost completely fills the blastocyst. The enlarging amniotic sac then presses upon and tends to collapse the yolk sac, and the embryonic half is invaginated into the abembryonic half, incomplete inversion, since the outer wall united to the trophoblast never entirely disappears.

The allantois arises later than in man. It reaches its maximum size in the 2.5 mm embryo. It is tubular and extends through the cord to the loose mesenchyme where the umbilical vessels spread under the placenta, then turns and runs laterally below the placenta for 0.75 mm more. It has a narrow lumen, at places a solid strand, and distally branches several times. In the 2.7 mm embryo the allantoic stalk has almost disappeared and is entirely absent in later stages.

There is early differentiation of the trophoblast into an inner cellular and an outer syncytial portion. The syncytiotrophoblast surrounds and erodes the maternal blood vessels, even the endometrium, and leaves the maternal blood in contact with the syncytial trophoblast, haemachorial. The placenta primarily diffuse becomes discoidal, labyrinthine and haemachorial and probably localized near the top of the fundal cavity.

Comment: The ovular decidual implantation here is complete with decidua basalis and decidua capsularis. This is similar to that of *Desmodus rotundus* with the exception that the two uterine horns have joined into one, producing a primitive simplex uterus with a tube-like canal rather than a slit-like cavity, and the fallopian tubes enter the top of the uterus and close together. As in the armadillo there probably is a very restricted mucosal area at the apex of the uterine canal in which implantation is possible.

In 1941, Wislocki and Fawcett described the placentas of several specimens of the Cuban phyllostomid bat, *Artebeus jamaicensis parvipes*. This bat possesses a uterus simplex consisting of a typical ovoid uterus and fallopian tubes which are remarkable by the fact that they penetrate the fundus of the uterus close together near the mediam line, instead of laterally as in other simplex uterine mammals. The relatively discoid chorioallantoic placenta is situated high on the dorsal wall. The extensive yolk sac lies compressed and flattened against the trophoblastic wall. The allantois is a simple diverticulum with its vessels vascularizing the trophoblast. There was a complete decidua capsularis indicating that the implantation was interstitial as was demonstrated previously by Hamlett, 1935, in another phyllostomid bat, *Glossophaga soricina* with a similar uterus and a true interstitial implantation.

The smooth umbilical cord had five vessels; two allantoic arteries and one vein and a vitelline artery and vein. The authors stated that the maternal blood traverses the lacunae, bathing the trophoblast directly and collects ultimately at the base of the placenta in a series of veins located in the decidual tissue beneath the labyrinth. They conclude that the placenta was labyrinthine and hemochorial, similar to that of Hamlett. However, in 1958, Wimsatt reported that there was present in these placentas an interstitial membrane barrier and thus the placenta was labyrinthine endotheliochorial and not hemochorial.

Comment: A comparison of the figure (11) of the bat *Desmodus rotundus* by Wimsatt, 1954, with the figure (12) of the phyllostomid bat *Glassophaga soricina* by Hamlett, 1934, presents a clear understanding of how uterus simplex of primates evolved from the bicornuate uterus of other mammals.

Robin, 1881, Wood Jones, 1917, and Matthews, 1941-44, investigated the genitalia of large series of bats. In summary, they found that the Pteropodidae had a tendency to two distinct uteri, each of which had its own cervix leading to the vagina. Furthermore, the vulvar opening was transverse on the perineum.

In the microchiropteran bats the uterus usually had a body and two cornua neither of which was very long. The single gestation seemed to favor the right horn. In some the blastocyst had a tendency to dilate its own horn and to herniate into the uterine body which then became the site of gestation in the later stages. There is one family, the *Phyllostomidae*, all with a simplex uterus; in these the vaginal opening is longitudinal on the perineum as in the human female. In all other microchiropteran bats the vagina opens onto the perineum transversely as in the megachiropteran Pteropodidae.

According to Matthews, great diversity of detail occurs in the genital anatomy of the Chiroptera and surprisingly wide differences are found in closely allied species. As pointed out by Robin (1881) and Wood Jones (1917), the only fairly homogeneous groups are the Megachiroptera and the Phyllostomidae. In the Megachiroptera the vaginal introitus is transverse. This is the situation also in many Microchiroptera, but in the Phyllostomidae the vulvar anatomy is very similar to that of the human female.

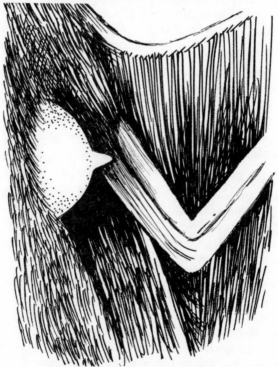

Fig. 13.—Paired mammary glands pectorally located in Brachyphylla cavernarum, a phyllostomid bat. Redrawn from F. Wood Jones, J. Anat. 51: 36-60, 1917.

Judging from their mode of placentation, the Megachiropteran bats, Pteropodidae, reached the level of at least partial interstitial decidual implantation of the blastocyst. Here their evolution ceased probably due to the mesometrial uterine site of implantation similar to that of the rodents who also, in this respect, were in a blind cul-de-sac. On the other hand most of the microchiropteran bats followed the course set by the insectivores and had antimesometrial uterine implantations. They were the ones chosen to further evolve interstitial implantation of the blastocyst and also finally to create the simplex uterus of the primates.

EYEWITNESS ACCOUNT OF THE BIRTH OF A BAT

Frederic Wood Jones, 1917, presented an eyewitness account of parturition in a bat. "A most interesting account of the parturition of a bat has been given by Mr. H. A. Blake, the then Governor of the Bahamas. The species on which the observations were made was said to be new to science, and I do not know if a determination of it was ever published. The female was one of a cave colony into which shots were fired to obtain specimens. She was picked up among those that fell, and was found to be alive and uninjured. She was confined in a cage, and during the next morning parturition commenced. The mother suspended herself by one foot only, and used the other to assist the process of birth. "The membranes presented, and the left hind limb of the fetus was the first part to be free of the maternal passages. The mother then used her free foot to rupture the membranes, and the liberated foot of the fetus at once grasped the leg of the mother. Ten minutes afterwards the other foot of the fetus was extruded, and this also grasped the mother's free leg. In another five minutes the whole fetus was entirely free of the maternal passages, it

123

being born with its dorsal surface anterior. Directly it was born the mother lowered the young one with her leg, licked it all over, and placed it at the breast, while it was still tethered by its umbilical cord.

"She bit through the cord, but carried out the process very slowly, not completing the severance till an hour after the young one was born. About ten hours after the birth of the young the placenta was extruded; the extrusion was assisted by the mother, and all of the constituents of the afterbirth were eaten. The young bats are born with their eyes closed, and they remain blind for some considerable time".

This was by breech presentation but some bat infants may be born head first.

IS IT NOT POSSIBLE THAT THE BATS WERE THE PROGENITORS OF PRIMATES?

Soon after Darwin, Huxley postulated that the insectivores presumably were the originators of the primate line and Hubrecht and Hill furthered this concept. It is here proposed that this position should be held not by the insectivores but by the bats which were closely related to the insectivores and had so many obvious primate characteristics that Linnaeus is said to have placed them with the primates.

All individual eutherian mammals, theoretically, have three consecutive placentas in each gestation (1) non-vascular trophoblast, prior to fetal vascularization (2) trophoblast, fetal yolk-sac vessel vascularized and (3) the definitive allantoic vascularized trophoblast, joined or not joined with the uterine mucosa to form the placenta. In many eutherian mammals the second (yolk-sac) placenta is deleted and when present in all others, it is detached in midgestation and obliterated by the definitive allantoic placenta.

In many bats, especially in microchiroptera as in the

closely allied insectivores, all three consecutive placentas occur in an antimesometrial area of the deciduous endometrial lining of the linear uterine lumen of one tube of the two uterine horns. In these bats and in the insectivores all three consecutive placentas are antimesometrial. In the relatively closely allied rodents, the last of the three placentas (the allantoic vascularized trophoblast) is markedly deviated and is transferred to the mesometrial side of the lumen, allowing the two previous antimesometrial placentas to atrophy. According to the investigations of Moghe, 1951, the placental site is mesometrial in the Megachiropteran *Pteropodidae*.

The insectivores produced a blastocyst that became almost completely surrounded by decidua but none ever was truly erosive into a self-made cavity in the mucosa outside of the uterine lumen. Such was accomplished only by the bats, and first in the vampire bat, *Desmodus*, investigated and reported upon by Wimsatt, 1954. This was similar to the method used by the Phyllostomid bats with simplex uteri.

It is postulated that the insectivores never could have produced a simplex uterus characteristic of the primates. The reason for this concept is that the individual insectivores were short-lived and could not reduce the possible large number of simultaneous gestations; thus the uterine horns remained long. On the other hand the bats lived up to 20 years and thus were able to reduce the individual gestations to one, or possibly two, embryos. This allowed the uterine horns to become shortened and finally to disappear into the simplex uterus. Such a situation can be found in no other group of deciduous eutherian mammals.

Following another line of reasoning, it is further suggested that no other central nervous system than that of bats could have been capable of being the foundation for that of man. All eutherian mammals except one group seem to have been quite satisfied with their early chosen ecological pursuits and did little experimentation. The great exception occurred in the bats. They were insectivorous but the insects took to the air. The bats, at tremendous expense of energy and ingenuity, evolved a self propelled body aeroplane to secure them in air but then they found that the insects flew mainly at night so they evolved echolocation. Some changed the ecology from insects to ripening fruit. One South American bat species, *Noctilio leporinus* catches and consumes water-borne top minnows. Another one, the vampire bat *Desmodus* created an unique ecology based upon blood from an artificial incision in the skin of a large mammal.

All of these varieties of ecological exploitations were accomplished by the precocious bats possibly within a few million years while it required 60 million years for man to evolve enough to learn the mechanisms used and to duplicate them by various extraneous machines. This is not to imply that there was any plan or conscious effort on the part of the bats but only that when genetic mutations led in these directions, their brains and central nervous systems were versatile enough to adapt readily to the consequences.

It is suggested that the simplex uterus would not have been practical prior to the evolution of a truly interstitial decidual implantation of the blastocyst because no blastocyst, per se, could enlarge enough to fill the expanded space in a simplex uterus and thus had to wait until such interstitial implantation was evolved in the decidua of one tube of a bicornuate uterus as was the case in *Desmodus*.

It is further postulated that eutherian mammals evolved in successive waves to the number of possibly eight. Members of each wave or level chose varying ecological pursuits for a livelihood. The first level possessed placentation similar to that of the ancestral viviparous reptiles whose more or less diffuse allantoic placental blastocyst matured within the lumen of a segment of one of the two bicornuate uterine tubes and subsisted upon uterine secretions. In each succeeding level there was more and more union of the allantoic placenta to the uterine mucosa, and the uterine mucosa evolved by becoming more and more receptive of such union, until in the final level, the blastocyst was capable of eroding a housing cavity within the deciduous mucosa and outside of the tubular lumen. When this stage had been reached, the two uterine horns subsequently disappeared into the simplex uterus of the primates.

According to their placentation the bats were polyphyletic and bats occurred in more than the latter half of these levels of evolution of the eutherian mammals. While most bats have allantoic placentation antimesometrial in site, as in insectivores, some such as Pteropodidae and a few Emballonuridae have such mesometrially located as in rodents.

THE MYSTERIES OF THE AFRICAN BUSH BABY, THE FLYING LEMUR AND OF THE AFRICAN GIANT WATER SHREW

A Belgian embryologist at the University of Brussels, Pol Gerard, began publishing investigations of placentation of bats and rodents about 1919. Gerard was professor of biology at the University of Brussels and was a publication editor of the Archives of Biology at Liege and Paris. This journal had been founded by Van Beneden and Van Bambeke. During the following dozen years he had the opportunity to study placentation in a female bush baby *Galago demidoffi*, a lemur-like mammal from central Africa. This specimen had been sent to him by the director of the museum of the Congo. Fixed in formalin, the bicornuate uterus contained a 28 mm long fetus in each of the two horns. Twins were reported to be rare in this species. The placentation appeared to be at marked variance from that which had been established over the previous fifty years for the Madagascar lemurs. It was central in a segment of the lumen of one of the two tubes of the bicornuate uterus, and the relationship to the uterine mucosa was epitheliochorial.

Because of this unusual discovery he induced the Belgian Royal Institute of Colonial Affairs to finance and permit him to head an expedition to the Congo to collect further specimens. On this mission he obtained six pregnant Galago females of the demidoffi species and several pregnant females of two other Galago species. *G. senegalensis moholi* and *G. crassicaudatus.*

All of these were reported in a rather extensive paper in 1932. This contained 51 illustrations, in some of which the labeling was somewhat inexplicable as noted by Mossman in 1937. The six specimens of *G. demidoffi* all had single embryos, which ranged from early implantation to a blastocyst of about 10 mm in diameter with several somites in the embryo. The implantation, well illustrated, showed the blastocyst to lie buried in decidua in manner very similar to that in the human pregnant uterus. The blastocyst lies centrally located in a sort of endometrial polypoid mound. Gerard did not state whether this was antimesometrial or mesometrial to the uterine lumen. He made an extensive comparison of this implantation with that of the human uterus as depicted by von Mollendorff.

The author stated that "in the course of development, all of the capsularis disappears and the freed trophoblast clings to the maternal epithelium: but there always persists a zone of implantation forming a decidua basalis. At this level the trophoblast differentiates into two beds, of which the external, formed of voluminous cells, puts itself in contact with the maternal vessels". I take this statement to mean that the

decidual cells disappeared, and the denuded trophoblast then joined with the mucosa (decidua vera) on
the abembryonic wall of the uterine lumen. His illustrations, 15, 17, 19 and 21, indicate this interpretation.
Furthermore, he went to great pains to demonstrate
the similarity to the human implantation.

From his description it may be concluded that the
placenta was villous and endotheliochorial. There is
little reason to suspect that the capsular chorion did
not join with the abembryonic decidua vera as it must
have in a similar situation in the vampire bat, Desmodus, and as it has been demonstrated to occur in the
human gestation. In *Galago demidoffi* and in
Desmodus, the gestations are interstitial in the mucosal
wall of slender uterine tubes, while in the human
gestation the similar situation occurs in a simplex
uterus with a relatively large cavity. Here the blastocyst, buried in one wall of the mucosa, must enlarge
enough to distend the large cavity rather than the
segment of a linear tubular uterus.

Simultaneously Gerard investigated the placentation
of two other Galago species, *Galago senegalensis moholi*
and *G. Crassicaudatus.* Furthermore. Mossman, 1937,
has summarized the investigation of *G. agisymbanus*
by Strahl. In all three of these Galago species the
placentation corresponded to the diffuse epitheliochorial type of the Madagascar lemurs as first described by Milne Edwards, 1875 and by Wm. Turner,
1878.

There is a possible and plausible solution to this
dilemma. Is it not conceivable that *Galago demidoffi*
was not derived from the lemurs but from the same
strain as that of the particular bat which has achieved
interstitial decidual implantation of the blastocyst?
This bat is the vampire bat, *Desmodus rotundus* as
described by Wimsatt in 1954. Thus, while still others
may be found, in all of the literature of investigation of

placentation there are only two mammals possessing a two-tubular uterus in which there occurred interstitial decidual implantation of the blastocyst. These two were the vampire bat and *Galago demidoffi*. At least three other species of Galagos have placentation more or less corresponding to the centrally implanted, epithelio-chorial placental lemurs.

There is another mammal which I suspect may be in a similar situation. This mammal, well illustrated in Walker's *Mammals of the World*, 1968, was of such diverse morphology that it could be fitted nowhere in the Linnaean classification and thus has been assigned an order of its own, the Dermoptera, of which, according to Walker, there are only two species. *Cynocephalus volans* inhabits the Philippine Islands and *C. variegatus*, southern Indo-China to the Malay States, Sumatra, Java and Borneo.

These flying lemurs are relatively large mammals, head and body length of 38 to 42 cm with additional 20 cm of tail. The gliding membrane extends from the neck to the tips of the fingers and toes along the sides of the body, and the interfemoral membrane incorporates the long tail. They are said to be helpless on the ground but are good tree climbers; climbing to great heights, they may glide to another tree 136 meters or more away and in the process lose no more than 10 or 12 meters of elevation.

The laterally and caudally extended membrane of reflected layers of body skin more resembles that of the bats than that of the gliding or flying squirrels. Although the fingers are at the ends of the arms and are not spread-out to form ribs of the membrane as in bats, the process by which the fingers became ribs of the membrane in bats may have been reversed in the creation of the gliding lemurs, but their essential mode of placentation was not altered. Not unlike some bats the diet is said to be fruits, buds, flowers and leaves.

Mossman has summarized the placentation of the Dermoptera under the name of *Galaeopithicus chombolis*. The implantation is antimesometrial in the lumen of one tube of the bicornuate uterus. The successive stages of placentation are discoid at the same site. The discoid allantoic placenta is transitional in microscopic morphology and is hemochorial. In the early stages there is a bilaminar omphalopleure, and the allantoic vesicle remains small. This is in conformity with some of the more complex placental insectivores or bats.

It is postulated that this mammal was modified from the strain that produced the more complex placental bats. Its highly evolved method of amniogenesis by cavitation rather than by folding is more similar to that of the bats than of the insectivores. Its mode of transporting its newborn infant, clinging to her abdominal fur and to the mammary nipples high on the chest is similar to that of some bats. If it has a bat-like tragus in its external ear the evidence should be augmented.

The stations in phylogeny of *Galago demidoffi* and of at least one species of Dermoptera may be assured by assuming that they each originated from the same source as the more complex placental bats to which their mode of placentation corresponds.

Another interesting type of placentation occurs in the giant watershrew, *Potamogale velox*. Walker stated that this mammal, classified as an insectivore, has an otter-like appearance, and its body measures 29 to 35 cm in length with a swimming tail about the same length. Apparently it does not use its legs in swimming. It is said to feed on crabs, fish and amphibians. Its habitat is in watery places from sea level to 1800 meters elevation in western and central equitorial Africa.

J. P. Hill, 1938, reported upon the unique placentation of this mammal, which he compared to the placentation of *Galago demidoffi,* except that in the Potamogale the uterus is simplex with non-functioning horns, and simultaneous gestations are limited to one or two. Apparently the implantation of the blastocyst was deeply interstitial to create a placenta hemochorialis diffusa with subsequent restriction to a discoid area. The trophoblast was solely fetal allantoic vascularized with the yolk-sac free and atrophied to a small mass in the exocoelom, outside of the amniotic cavity. These features are quite typical of some primate placentations. Furthermore in this mammal the allantoic sac, which is large tends to divide into four compartments. In the simplex uterine armadillo there is a division of the primarily common amnion and of the allantoic placenta, but here each separated compartment houses an individual embryo.

Is it not possible that Potamogale is more closely allied to the phyllostomid bats, whose placentation, in a similar simplex uterus, quite parallels its own?

It is conceivable that the three African mammals whose placentations have been described were closely allied to respective levels of bats from whom they received their placentation methods.

All three of these mammals here are considered to have been closely related in placentation to, and to have originated from the same strains that produced certain bats. They did not choose the ecology of bats securing insects or arthropoda flying in air but chose an ecology on the ground, or by gliding in air, or by swimming in water. Thus during 60 million years they lost the wing span of the bats but retained the placentation.

EUTHERIAN MAMMALIAN EVOLUTION

In consideration of the evolution within the allantoic placental eutherian mammalian line, it is absolutely requisite that the first level of such mammals have placentation very similar to that of the viviparous reptiles who had achieved a diffuse allantoic placenta and who were the immediate ancestors. This proposition cannot be denied with any validity.

It has been demonstrated that in the viviparous reptiles, the allantoic vascularized, trophoblastic placenta was essentially diffuse, thus, surrounding and covering most of the blastocyst which, still lay relatively free in its segment of the linear cavity of one of the two uterine horns (central implantation).

It may accurately be stated that the allantoplacental blastocyst was perfected by the allantoplacental viviparous reptiles. The sole embryonic evolution that occurred in the whole line of eutherian mammals was confined to how to manage and care for this already perfected blastocyst within the maternal uterus which, as in the ancestral viviparous reptiles, was bicornuate. This control began as simple but extended to complex, from mere housing of the blastocyst within a segment of the lumen of one tube of a bicornuate uterus to complete burial of the blastocyst in the uterine mucosal deciduous wall of one horn of a bicornuate uterus. This was first accomplished in the vampire bat, *Desmodus*. The final step was the creation of the simplex uterus by the Phyllostomid bats in which also there was interstitial decidual burial of the blastocyst.

One readily notes that this process required increasing aggressiveness on the part of the blastocyst coincidental with evolutionary change in structure of the uterine mucosa to acquiesce to this embryonic invasion. This process occurred in stages. Whenever a stage advanced enough to create a more efficient line of mammals there arose a new level, but the individuals had to be able to compete or become extinct. These levels from the simplest in the bicornuate uterus to the most complex in the simplex uterus are individually described in the following pages. The most active eutherian mammals in this respect were the bats, principally Microchiroptera, who were the first to have interstitial decidual burial of the blastocyst and the first and only ones to evolve the simplex uterus. Not only were they extremely inventive in embryology but they were the most creative in exploiting new and strange ecologies. Some of these required a supreme degree of ingenuity especially in respect to flight in air.

Thus, in the first wave or level of these mammals the 'space capsule' blastocyst, containing the embryo soon to become a fetus, lies freely in the lumen of one of the two uterine horns. A German biologist Otto Grosser at the beginning if this century named this type of placentation epitheliochorial (the chorial trophoblast covering the blastocyst lay next to and facing but not attaching to the epithelial lining of the uterine mucosa).

From the records of placentation in the literature all of those mammals with this type were identified. These are: Eastern American moles (*Scalopus aquaticus*), Madagascar lemurs, pigs, horses, rhinoceroses hippopoptamuses, whales, dolphins and porpoises. The scaly ant-eaters (pangolins, Pholidota) may have been in this level.

This group of mammals thus, cannot avoid having been the first wave or level of eutherian mammals. They all subsisted upon uterine gland secretions (uterine milk) poured into the space around the blastocyst covered by its diffuse allantoic placenta, completely fetal without maternal parts.

A mare's placenta when spread out on the ground covers an area about the size of a 5 by 5 foot rug and is about as thick throughout except at two areas that had covered the two ends of the blastocyst as it lay in the linear uterine canal. Here, there is atrophy, and thinning localized to these two sites. From the um-

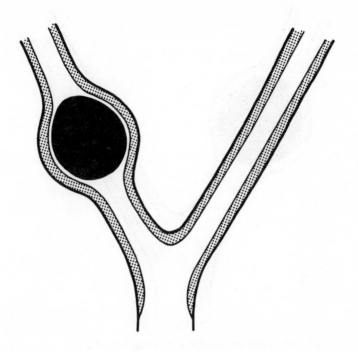

Fig. 14.—Eutherian mammalian evolutionary level 1.

The blastocyst, diffusely allantoic vascularized, lies free in the lumen of one tube of a bicornuate uterus, Grosser epitheliochorial.

This occurs in allantoplacental viviparous reptiles and in the first level of eutherian mammals, to wit: Eastern American mole, **Scalopus aquaticus**, lemurs, pigs, horses, hippopotamuses, rhinoceroses, whales, dolphins and porpoises.

bilical cord, fetal vessels ramify throughout the placenta and into tiny villi on the maternal surface. When the foal is born, there is no maternal bleeding because the placenta does not unite with the lining of the mother's uterus. This is similar to the relationship of a bird's egg to the lining of the maternal reproductive tract. This same situation applies in the pregnancy and delivery of the fetus in a whale or in all others of this first level of eutherian mammals.

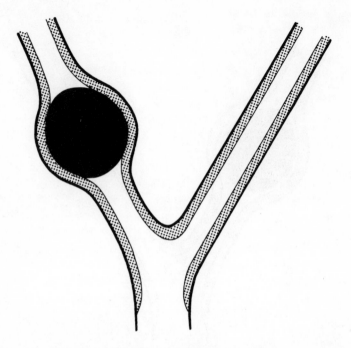

Fig. 15.—Eutherian mammalian evolutionary level 2.

The blastocyst, diffusely allantoic vascularized, lies central in the lumen of one uterine horn. Here there is some connection to the uterine mucosal wall, Grosser syndesmochorial. It is here presumed that this composes the second level in the evolution of the eutherian mammals comprising many artiolactyla: camels, deer, giraffes, sheep, goats, cattle and antelopes.

The second wave of these eutherian mammals in their evolution had a similar placenta, still diffuse, but here there was some actual connection of the chorionic trophoblast to the uterine lining. This was in the form of fetal vascularized nodules (cotyledons) on the trophoblast, and these nodules fitted into depressed holes in the uterine mucosa, some of whose epithelial covering may have been destroyed. Grosser termed this type syndesmochorial. Thus in the second level of these mammals there was increased feto-maternal exchange. From a review of the placentation literature the mammals which possessed this second type of placentation are the artiodactyla (cows, sheep, deer, goats, camels etc.).

By now the available land masses of the earth were covered by these two waves of vegetarian and peaceful, warm-blooded mammals able to avoid the declining, cold-blooded reptiles. The next wave of mammals, logically were the carnivores, whose food supply became the already processed plant life in the bodies of these vegetarian, previous inhabitants of the land. Thus the placentation of this third wave or level was merely an extension of that of the second wave. The allantoic vascularized trophoblastic placenta still was primarily diffuse but here there became actual erosion of the uterine mucosa by the trophoblast to form a deciduous placenta (one that sheds maternal as well as fetal tissue). It so happens that this particular type of diffuse placenta with its intermingling of fetal blood vessels lying in ridges or sometimes villi of fetal tissue next to the endothelial lining of the maternal capillaries, was feasible because the protective uterine tissue had been eroded away by the fetal trophoblast. Grosser designated this as endotheliochorial (the chorial trophoblast vessels lay close to the maternal endothelial vessel walls).

This type of placenta, unknown before, was extremely effective in transferring food, oxygen and water from the maternal tissues to the fetal tissues. Thus, so much placenta was unnecessary. The logical result was to restrict the diffuse placenta during gestation by atrophy of the placenta on the two ends of the blastocyst so that there remained an active band of placenta around the middle of the blastocyst in which lay the fetus. Thus, carnivores usually are characterized by a girdle shaped placenta at term. Rarely restriction was carried further to one or two disks. In addition to the carnivores one particular type of bat, Molossidae, *Tadarida brasiliensis cynocephala* (Stephens, 1962) appears to possess this restricting

137

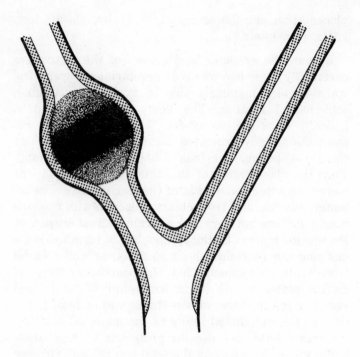

Fig. 16.—Eutherian mammalian evolutionary level 3.

The blastocyst, diffusely allantoic vascularized, lies central in the lumen of one uterine horn and the trophoblast makes intercellular connection with the deciduous uterine mucosa, Grosser endothelio-chorial. This creates so much maternal fetal exchange that such an extensive placenta is unnecessary. Consequently the placental tissue on the two ends of the blastocyst atrophies and usually a girdle placenta results. These features characterize the carnivores. The molossid bat, investigated by Stephens, 1962, appears to possess a similar carnivore type of placentation.

type of primarily diffuse endotheliochorial placenta. In addition, it has a sort of accessory placental sac containing maternal blood, common in the carnivore placenta. A few other bats have the same situation.

These three levels of eutherian mammals here are considered to comprise the first one third of eutherian mammalian evolution beginning with non-attachment of the diffuse placenta to the uterine mucosa but lying free and central in the uterine canal and from here on to the stages in which the diffuse allantoic placenta erodes the uterine mucosa down to the endothelial lining of the maternal capillaries (deciduous type of blastocyst implantation).

Only in the last portion of this first third of eutherian mammalian evolution did the fetal yolk-sac vessels take part in creating the temporary, secondary yolk-sac placenta; this occurred in the carnivores, comprising the third level of eutherian mammals.

In those mammals, with central implantation of the blastocyst, as the blastocyst grew in size, the surrounding uterine wall grew simultaneously and the placenta at any point never lost its exact original apposition to the uterine mucosa. Thus, very large animals readily were produced. This was similar to the dinosaur reptiles; all they were required to do was to lay a larger egg in its blastocyst to be matured outside of the mother's body.

With the beginning of the second third of eutherian mammalian evolution there occurred a most drastic alteration of placentation. It has been demonstrated that at the end of the first third of such there originally was too much functional placenta that became so very active. In these the placental restriction occurred during each gestation but *in the onset of the second third, the restriction in area of placentation took place prior to the implantation of the blastocyst.* In the second third of evolution of these mammals the diffuse trophoblast covering of the blastocyst was reduced to one area to be fetally vascularized to form a localized and usually primarily discoid placenta. This vascularized area, only, became attached to the uterine mucosal wall to form a primarily discoid placenta in rodents, insectivores and some bats. Thus, during this middle third of evolution of the eutherian mammals, the placenta was localized and discoid. Here, also were three consecutive placentas

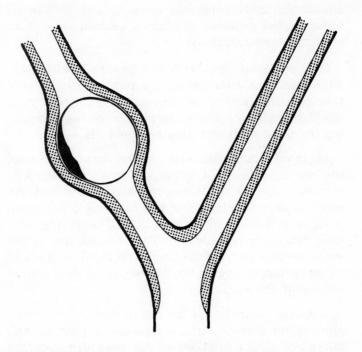

Fig. 17.—Level 4. Since the trophoblast endotheliochorial attachment was so effective it became unnecessary to vascularize the whole of the spherical potential trophoblast as previously. Thus in level 4 only a discreet area was fetal vascularized. In this level the blastocyst still became central in the lumen of one uterine horn but only a small and usually discoid area became fetal vascularized and attached to the uterine mucosa. So far the mammals which have these features appear to be the tarsier, the rabbit and the vespertilionid bat.

in each gestation, (1) primary trophoblastic attachment prior to development of fetal vessels, (2) the second placenta in the trophoblast vascularized by the fetal yolk-sac vessels and (3) the final placenta, allantoic fetal vascularized trophoblast which then allowed atrophy of the previous two.

In eutherian mammalian level 4 the blastocyst still should lie centrally in its segment of the canal of one of the two uterine horns, but its localized area placenta should attach to the mucosa lining the uterine cavity. Such a situation appears in three mammals so far recorded as to their placentation, the rabbit, the tarsier and the vespertilionid bat.

According to Amoroso's resume of the implantation of the rabbit, the definitive allantoic (split) placenta is located mesometrially in a segment of the lumen of one tube of a bicornuate uterus. A previous yolk-sac placenta formed here but became completely inverted.

From Hubrecht's work, interpreted by Hill, 1932, the tarsier blastocyst appears to have trophoblast activated at only one discoid area which attaches mesometrially to the uterine mucosa in the lumen of a segment of one uterine horn. Thus there is formed a primary, non-fetal vascularized, discoid placenta. The amnion covered embryo with its dependent yolk-sac is in the opposite portion of the developing blastocyst which enlarges centrally in the uterine horn lumen. Apparently, off of the caudal portion of the yolk-sac a diverticulum develops and extends in the direction of the träger-like trophoblastic attachment. Thus this trophoblastic area is allantoic vascularized and no yolk-sac placenta develops. The definitive allanto-choronic placenta is mesometrial as in rodents and unlike the insectivores and most bats.

The antimesometrial placentation of the Vespertilionid bat *Myotis* has been described in the chapter on Chiroptera (Wimsatt, 1944).

Level 5 (fig. 18) may be considered to comprise the rodents numbering 6,400 species. In each gestation they have three consecutive placentas. The first one is not yet fetal vascularized trophoblast which makes an antimesometrial attachment to the uterine mucosa. The second placenta, yolk-sac vessel vascularized trophoblast appears at the same antimesometrial site but the definitive allantoic vascularized placenta (the third and final placenta) lies to the mesometrial side of the uterine canal. This aberration possibly cost them the opportunity to cooperate in any future embryological evolution. Their own future evolution con-

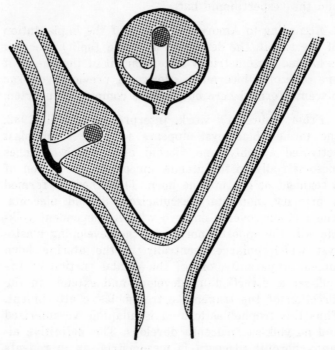

Fig. 18.—In level 5 with the uterine mucosa very active the trophoblast implants in a crypt in the linear tubular lumen. In each gestation the primary placenta is unvascularized trophoblast. The secondary placenta is yolk-sac vessel vascularized and the third and definitive placenta is allantoic vascularized which allows atrophy of the previous yolk-sac placenta. In rodents and in megachiropteran bats the definitive allantoic placenta is mesometrial in site.

sisted of modifications of this basic mode of placentation received possibly 60 million years ago from the embryological main stem of evolution.

The rodents appear to be a blind pouch branched off from the main line of embryological evolution. Individually and reproductively they were very successful, and their ecology did not diminish (in fact increased). Their life span was short so they never could afford to reduce the number of gestations to one at a time. Thus they could not evolve the simplex uterus as did the bats.

The closest they came to producing an interstitial implantation of the blastocyst was in the guinea pig, where the blastocyst was covered almost entirely by deciduous mucosa, but this was not a burial, erosive type which was necessary to the evolution of the simplex uterus. They never evolved further and had no chance to do so. In this respect they were somewhat like the sharks, the birds and even the marsupials.

It was not the rodents nor the insectivores, per se, but the insectivorous bats, changed to fruit bats, which carried the future evolution.

The rodents appear to have been committed to a mesometrial site for the definitive allantoic placenta while future evolution lay in exploitation of the anti-mesometrial site for this placenta.

Level 6 (fig. 19) may be considered to comprise certain insectivores and certain bats, all with antimesometrial implantation of all three stages of the primarily discoid placenta. Here there were varying degrees of interstitial trophoblastic invasion of the uterine mucosa until deep burial in the bicornuate uterus of the vampire bat.

Level 7 (fig. 20) in the vampire bat, *Desmodus rotundus*, studied by Wimsatt, 1954, indicated true interstitial burial type of blastocyst invasion of the uterine deciduous mucosa. This type also has been reported by Pol Gerard, 1932, to occur in *Galago demi-doffi,* an African lemur-like mammal which, because of its placentation may be more closely related to the vampire bat.

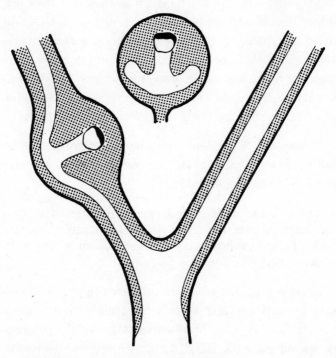

Fig. 19.—In level 6, comprising the insectivores and their allied microchiropteran bats the definitive allantoplacenta is located anti-mesometrially in the uterine tube. This feature is important because future evolution favored the antimesometrial site.

Level 8, (fig. 21) (the final one) is considered to comprise those mammals with two characteristics (1) partial or deep, interstitial implantation of the blastocyst and (2) possession of a simplex uterus. The simplex uterus was predicated upon two previous occurrences: (1) interstitial implantation of the blasto-

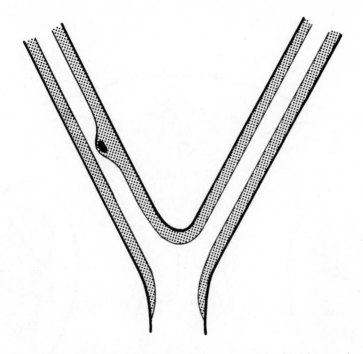

Fig. 20.—In level 7 for the first time there occurred a burial type of blastocyst implantation into deciduous mucosa. This appeared in the bicornuate uterine vampire bat, Desmodus, and also in the African bush baby, Galago demidoffi.

cyst into decidua lining the canal of one of the two horns of a bicornuate uterus, and (2) reduction in the number of simultaneously developed eggs at each gestation so that the uterine horns may become shortened to finally disappear in the single uterine body.

It may be added that this evolution did not occur in the short-lived insectivores which could not afford to reduce the number of young at a time, but this did occur only in the bats, the adults of which may live up to 20 years or more. *Thus, the bats can be the only*

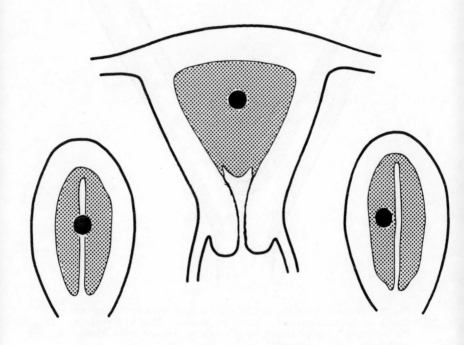

Fig. 21.—In level 8 for the first time appeared the simplex uterus and this first occurred in the phyllostomid bats. Here there may be Grosser endotheliochorial attachment or in some groups, hemochorial. The mammals with these features in varying degrees are: the phyllostomid bats, armadillos, sloths, anteaters, African giant water shrews, marmosets, monkeys, apes and mankind.

possible originators of the simplex uterus. This probably first occurred in the phyllostomid bats which also had blastocyst interstitial, decidual implantation. Therefore it is concluded that all simplex uterine mammals must have originated from these bats.

SUMMARY

For those who do not desire to consider the details, the following is what, essentially, is concluded to have happened to eventuate into man and the other primates. At first, in the evolution of the eutherian line of mammals, the placenta (as in the immediately ancestral viviparous reptiles) was diffuse over the blastocyst, central in the uterine canal without any attachment other than apposition. Following this, attachment began between the trophoblast (covering the blastocyst) and the uterine mucosal lining of the canal to produce the second level and increased in the third level to such an extent that no longer was a diffuse placenta necessary. In these the diffuse placenta became restricted in area during gestation. These events comprised the first third of eutherian evolution.

In the second third of such evolution, placental restriction to one localized area on the diffuse trophoblast occurred prior to implantation. Thus only one area of the surface of the blastocyst attached to the uterine mucosa and this primarily discoid placenta was characteristic of the rodents, insectivores and some bats. In all of these the yolk-sac was revived to create the second of three consecutive placentas in each gestation.

The final third of eutherian mammalian evolution was characterized by the development of the simplex uterus, formed by shortening and disappearance of the two uterine horns into the single body. Here, the trophoblast again became diffusely active and began to develop interstitial implantation into deciduous mucosa. This was not original here but had first occurred in one of the two uterine horns in the vampire bat. Shallow or deep interstitial implantation became characteristic of all simplex uterine mammals; phyllostomid bats, African giant water shrews, armadillos, Central American sloths and anteaters, South American marmosets, monkeys, apes and mankind.

If they are lucky, medical students may learn something about how the human blastocyst implants interstitially into uterine decidua but, in general, there is little realization that this supreme accomplishment was the final stage in several hundred million years of previous, step by step, preparation of the blastocyst and the uterine mucosa for such a magnificent event.

INTERRELATIONSHIP OF EUTHERIAN MAMMALS

Based upon the blastocyst capsule (containing the egg and future embryo-fetus) and its relationship to the maternal uterine canal or its mucosal wall, interrelationship of the eutherian mammals should appear somewhat as follows: (Hyraxes, *Hyracoidea*, dugongs and manatees, *Sirenia*, and elephants, *Proboscidea*, all possess a similar blastocyst central implantation in the uterine canal and the placentation varies markedly during gestation). These mammals tentatively are placed, intervening between level 2 and level 3.

Primates (simplex uterine mammals) phyllostomid bats, African giant water shrews, armadillos, sloths, anteaters, marmosets, monkeys, apes and mankind.

8th Wave or Level

Vampire bats, Galago demidoffi

7th Wave or Level

Several bats, flying lemur (Dermoptera)

6th Wave or Level

Rodents, insectivores and some bats

5th Wave or Level

Rabbits, tarsiers and Vespertilionid bats

4th Wave or Level

Carnivores, cats, dogs, bears, seals, walruses etc., Molossid bats

3rd Wave or Level

Artiodactyla, cattle, sheep, goats, deer, camels, etc.

2nd Wave or Level

American mole, lemurs, pigs, horses, hippopotamuses, rhinoceroses, dolphins, porpoises, and whales (possibly scaly ant-eaters)

1st Wave or Level

Allantoic placental viviparous reptiles

Basic Foundation

SUGGESTED EMBRYOLOGICAL EVOLUTION OF EUTHERIAN MAMMALS

Note. Their mode of placentation suggests that Hyracoidea, Sirenia and Proboscidea may have formed a link between level 2 and level 3: between Artiodactyla and Carnivora.

A simplification may be better visualized. For the first half of the 700 million years of animal life on earth the multiple-celled animals reproduced by the simple yolked egg. This was a speck of living protoplasm lightly bound by the maternal ovary to a variable quantity of yolk (food for the embryo). The evolving embryo, relatively naked in the water, surrounded the yolk with a gut sac to form the yolk-sac. As the yolk was used up the enlarging embryo could obtain food by mouth from the environment to further development into an intermediate larval stage or to a tiny replica of one of its parents.

The direct descendants of all animals which used this method continue to employ the same. Many of these are oviparous in water but some are viviparous. In these, the watery environment is composed of uterine secretions in which the embryo swims inside of the uterus. When fully matured the fetus is expelled from the maternal reproductive tract to the outside water.

About 350 million years ago vertebrates began to emerge from water to live on land. Unlike the invertebrates, the vertebrates could not use the simple yolked (anamniote) egg to reproduce on land without going back to water for maturation of the egg in water. The solution to the problem was to provide the simple yolked egg with a private pool of water for the embryo, adding a new gut sac, the allantois, for waste products and to cover all with trophoblast to create the blastocyst. This was done in the advanced amphibians and then bequeathed to the reptiles and from them to birds, monotremes, marsupials and to eutherian mammals. Since the private pool of water was enclosed in amnion all of these are known as amniote animals and are the only ones on earth in which the egg is no longer simple yolked, but is housed in the blastocyst which then becomes the unit. A bird's egg is a potential blastocyst. *In all viviparous reptiles and in all mam-*

mals it is not the egg which implants, but it is the egg in its house (the blastocyst) which implants.

For many millions of years in the reptiles the blastocyst was covered by a shell and matured outside of the maternal body. This was the method bequeathed to the warm-blooded birds and to the monotremes. The reptiles advanced to ovoviviparity where the shell covered egg was retained in the maternal reproductive tract to hatch out and be born alive. The reptiles further advanced to true viviparity with deletion of the shell and development of a trophoblastic placenta fetal vascularized by yolk-sac vessels. This they gave to the marsupial mammals. This proved to be rather unsatisfactory so the reptiles further advanced to viviparity with a fetal allantoic vascularized trophoblastic placenta. The reptiles retained this blastocyst in a pool of uterine secretions in a segment of the uterine lumen. This perfected blastocyst and its simple method of management was presented to the eutherian line of mammals whose evolution depended upon successive stages of management of the blastocyst within the maternal uterine cavity and its mucosal (eventually deciduous) wall.

In the allantoic vascularized placenta of the eutherian mammals what happened to the yolk-sac?

In the first two levels the yolk-sac produced a large fluid-filled cavity within the blastocyst, but it seldom reached to nor did it ever vascularize the trophoblast. Thus there was no secondary yolk-sac placental stage. However, in the third level comprising the carnivores there appeared three consecutive placentas in each gestation (1) trophoblast prior to the formation of the fetal circulation, (2) trophoblast, vascularized by fetal yolk-sac vessels, and (3) the definitive allantoic placenta (trophoblast, fetal-allantoic-vessel-vascularized) which by mid-term had obliterated the secondary yolk-sac placenta.

It appears that the early and temporary yolk-sac placenta began to assert itself in the third level (carnivora) of eutherian mammalian evolution. According to Mossman, there was a temporary yolk-sac placenta in dogs (Canidae), racoons (Procyon lotor), pole cat (Putorius furo), cat (Felidae), lions and seals. In all carnivora, however, the blastocyst lay central in the lumen of one of two uterine horns and its diffuse surface trophoblast, definitely vascularized by allantoic vessels, made attachment to the covering uterine mucosa which was 'invaded to form the diffuse endotheliochorial placenta.

This diffuse placenta was so highly active in maternal fetal transport that during each gestation its surface area became restricted to either a circumscribing middle band, or even further to one or two discoid areas. This situation, then, preceded the next levels of eutherian mammals, the rodents and the insectivores with their offshoots, some of the bats. In these mammals the trophoblast became active on its surface at only one area usually discoid, which then implanted locally to the uterine mucosa.

In the last third of eutherian mammalian evolution (simplex uterine mammals) the yolk-sac vessels never vascularized the trophoblast. Thus, as in most of the first third, the secondary yolk-sac placenta never developed in the simplex uterine mammals. The temporary yolk-sac placenta was characteristic principally of the middle third of such evolution. This comprised the rodents, insectivores and some bats.

According to various papers which recently have appeared in *Scientific American* the continental land masses were one unit about 200 million years ago. Fifteen of these articles have been edited by J. Tuzo Wilson in a volume, *Continents Adrift*, 1972. During the Mesozoic era the continents began to separate. Apparently the first to break off was Australia together

152

with Antarctica. This must have been at a stage of animal evolution in which the only mammals so far evolved on earth were monotremes and marsupials which thus became isolated in Australia. Many million years later South America presumably became separated from Africa when the earth was populated by these two groups of primitive mammals plus the first level of eutherian mammals but without eutherian carnivores. South America then became separated from Africa by the Atlantic ocean and South America was separated from North Amercia by the Bolivar Trench which joined the Atlantic and the Pacific oceans.

However, there is early fossil evidence of apparently simplex uterine mammals in all three continents. The problem is how did these latest evolved eutherian mammals, soon after their origin, simultaneously appear in all three isolated continents, Africa, South America and North America? It is here postulated that the simplex uterine mammals all arose from the simplex uterine Phyllostomid bats which conceivably could have colonized all three continents by flight, aided by storm winds. In North America they apparently became extinct but according to Romer their fossils demonstrate that they were similar to but not identical to edentates, (simplex uterine armadillos, sloths and anteaters) of South America.

Probably the distance intervening then was far less than at the present time, and presumably not much more than twice the distance from Africa to Madagascar, which is said to be the home of Myzopodidae with sessile adhesive pads or disks on the wrists or ankles. This vespertilionid bat originally must have arrived there by being air borne. Walker stated that an individual of the genus *Artibeus*, of the family Phyllostomidae, presumably wind-blown, has been taken at Key West, Florida. This is about 300 miles from Jamaica.

Furthermore Walker lists five families of bats, in-

153

cluding 14 genera which had colonized Australia but none were among the Phyllostomidae.

In his classification of mammals, Simpson noted fossilized bats from the Oligocene period in Australia.

Thus the bats probably arrived in isolated South America possibly 50 million years prior to the eruption of the land bridge from North America to South America. Here the phyllostomids could have planted the simplex uterine primates competing only with the marsupials and peaceful, primitive, eutherian mammals. The only carnivores were among the marsupials, some of which became formidable. Eutherian carnivores had to wait until the land bridge which came, according to Romer, with the Pliocene period a few million years ago. He stated that then followed an invasion by North American eutherian mammals including eutherian carnivores. These probably included the saber-toothed tiger and the primitive eutherian ungulates of South America fared poorly and this extremely numerous assemblage vanished entirely. On the other hand, many families of simplex uterine mammals, as well as the marsupials with the exception of their carnivores, did much better and exist today in South America. In recent times some of them have crossed the land bridge into North America.

There is paleontological evidence that eutherian (allantoplacental) mammals existed 180 million years ago. For the first 120 million years, during the Mesozoic era, these furtive mammals sharpened their wits trying to keep out of the way of the reigning reptiles (plus birds, amphibians, monotremes and marsupials). It may be presumed that they possessed diffuse placentas, allantoic vascularized on the outer surface of the blastocyst which lay central in a segment of one tube of a bicornuate tubular uterus and subsisted by absorption of uterine gland secretions (level one).

About 60 million years ago, with the decline of the

154

reptiles, the eutherian mammals began a significant evolution based upon renewed activity of the blastocyst to invade the single tubular uterine wall. This was associated with compliance on the part of the uterine mucosa in alteration allowing this progressive invasion. The combined result was increased opportunity for maternal-fetal exchange superior to that provided simply by uterine gland secretions absorbed by the naked allantochorionic trophoblast.

In this direction, after seven successive steps creating all of the subsequent eutherian mammals, the blastocyst was able to bury itself completely into uterine decidual mucosa in a newly created simplex uterus.

While the first level reached back into the Mesozoic era, paleontology reveals that none of the subsequent levels were in existence earlier that the Eocene period.

MONKEYS	MANKIND
(duplex placental)	(usually single placental)
MARMOSETS	APES
(duplex placental)	(usually single placental)
ANTEATERS	MONKEYS
SLOTHS	(usually single placental)
ARMADILLOS	AFRICAN GIANT
IN SOUTH AMERICA	WATER SHREW
(some in North America)	IN AFRICA

PHYLLOSTOMID BATS
(The first mammals to possess a simplex uterus
some 60 million years ago)

SUGGESTED EVOLUTION OF
SIMPLEX UTERINE PRIMATES

Romer also described early Cenozoic edentate (armadillo, sloth and anteater) fossils from North

America. These were similar to but not identical to those from South America. If those had simplex uteri, as they probably did, they must have received such from the only possible source, the phyllostomid bats which simultaneously may have colonized North America as well as South America and Africa to originate simplex uterine mammals at the same time in three continents separated by wide seas. Apparently those in North America early became extinct, possibly unable to complete with the evolving eutherian mammals there, including many which were carnivorous.

The radiation in North America became extinct so only inferences can be made in respect to the placentation. However, in Africa and in South America each radiation evolved all theoretically possible variations of blastocyst-decidual relationships, but only that in Africa led to the evolution of man. Phyllostomid bats continue to live in South America and neighboring regions, but, according to Walker, they became extinct in Africa in the Oligocene period of the Cenozoic era.

It is interesting to note the close similarity of placentation and morphology of the individual monkeys of South America with those which evolved independently in Africa.

One might consider the hypothesis that simplex uterine eutherian mammals (primates) originated simultaneously in three continents separated by fairly wide seas. These three continents were Africa, South America and North America. This situation arose from the first mammal to evolve the simplex uterus, *the phyllostomid bat* which could be air borne to the various isolated places in which these simplex uterine lines originated.

In Africa this apparently led through the African giant water shrew, single placental monkeys, apes and mankind. In South America it led through the Xenarthra (armadillos, sloths and anteaters) and duplex placenta monkeys. In North America only the Xenarthra evolved but having to compete with the developing lines of other eutherian mammals they became extinct here within a few million years.

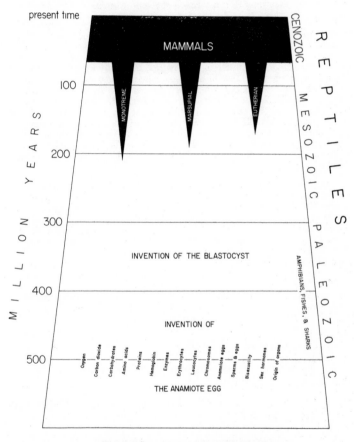

ORIGIN OF MAMMALS

Fig. 22.—The three groups of mammals, Monotremata, Marsupalia and Eutheria had their origins deep in the Mesozoic era. As had birds previously the monotremes arose as a warm-blooded offshoot of the egg laying reptiles which remained cold-blooded. The marsupials arose from the reptiles when these had acquired viviparity with a yolk-sac vessel vascularized placenta. Subsequently when the reptiles had achieved viviparity with an allantoic vascularized placenta they gave origin to the warm-blooded fur-covered eutherian line.

The viviparous allantoic placental reptiles perfected the blastocyst but it remained central and free in the lumen of one tube of the bicornuate uterus. This was presented to the first level of the eutherian mammals. **Eutherian mammalian evolution comprised the progressive intrauterine management of this already perfected blastocyst.** In addition the bicornuate uterus finally became simplex for primates.

There is evidence that Australia and Antarctica were separated from Pangaea in the Mesozoic era when the only mammals so far evolved were monotremes and marsupials. Thus these were well able to evolve further in Australia free from competition with eutherian mammals, especially eutherian carnivores, the only carnivores there being marsupial. Some few million years later South America became separated from Africa but after the first (and possibly some second level of) eutherian mammals had appeared but before the third level comprising the eutherian carnivores. At the time of separation, South America should have been capable of receiving monotremes, marsupials and level 1 eutherian mammals as well as all animals developed previously. Presumably monotremes became extinct there as elsewhere excepting in Australia but some day fossilized remains should be found.

It is postulated that the eutherian mammals in the root-spur into the mesozoic era were most closely allied to the allanto-placental reptiles in the mode of placentation. They probably were limited to eutherian mammalian level (1) with the allanto-placental blastocyst central and free in the lumen of one of the two uterine horns. Such occurs in the Eastern American mole, **Scalopus aquaticus,** lemurs, pigs, horses, hippopotamuses; rhinoceroses, dolphins and whales. From Romer's description of the South American fossilized ungulates it appears that they were remotely related to primitive horses, rhinoceroses and hippopotamuses and it might be presumed that their placentation was similar. Note. Many of the items listed on line five hundred million years, were in existence previously for one hundred and fifty million years or more.

HUMAN PLACENTATION

There are myriads of depths of implantation into the decidua available to the human blastocyst. Those employed may be collected into five groups, described by Torpin, 1968.

(1) The blastocyst lies between the two flat sheets of decidua, ventral and dorsal, where it invades both sheets, in the simplex uterus at first diffusely, but subsequently evolving a placenta duplex. The fetus then has two discoid placentas, a primary one to which the umbilical cord attaches and a secondary one on the opposite wall of the blastocyst lying in the uterine

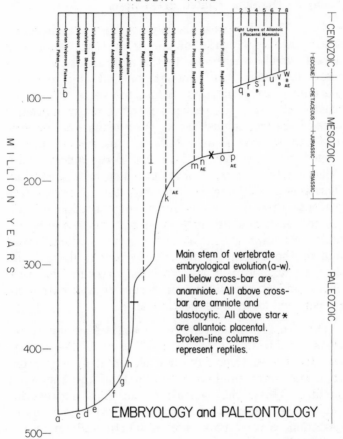

Fig. 23.—Note. Underneath the distal end of the main stem line of evolution the letter B denotes the occurrence of bats. The letters A E represent anteaters.

cavity. Fetal blood vessels extend in the membranes from one disk to the other. This situation with the development of a normal full term fetus occurs once per thousand human pregnancies and also possibly in the great apes who, as in human female, usually have a single placenta. This is the method employed in general in all marmosets and in 75 per cent of macaque implantations and in many New World monkeys. As in man there is reason to believe that it may also occur rarely in the near-related great apes.

(2)   The blastocyst usually implants antimesometrially into near center of one of the two, ventral or dorsal, sheets of decidua in the simplex uterus. Normally it buries itself enough so that the resulting placenta is reduced from diffuse to one fourth of the blastocyst wall. This restriction to the active placental area of the trophoblast facing the uterine wall maternal blood supply occurs while the blastocyst still is buried in the mucosa at one site in the uterine wall. When the blastocyst, at about two months of gestation, increases in volume to fill the uterine cavity, the placenta then covers one fourth of the uterine wall. As the gestation advances to term, the placenta remains constant at one fourth of the blastocyst wall and of the uterine cavity. Consequently, there is no disruption of villi at the placental margin. This produces perfect apposition and occurs in approximately 60 per cent of human gestations.

(3)   In approximately 30 per cent of human gestations the blastocyst buries itself a little deeper into the decidua so that the early placental area is more than one fourth and up to one half of the blastocyst surface. When this gestation sac fills the uterine cavity, the placenta, at approximately two months of gestation, covers more than a fourth and up to one half of the uterine cavity. In this situation, throughout the remainder of gestation, the margin of this excess-area-placenta gradually is withdrawn from its decidual bed. The detached villi atrophy and help form a white deposit around the edge of the enlarging definitive placenta. This is known as placenta marginata. The reduction is gradual, and eventually the placenta covers the usual one fourth of the uterine cavity at term. The marginal villous disruption from the decidual bed causes decidual hemorrhage, which may quickly clot and be innocuous or may induce spontaneous abortion

or later in gestation, premature separation of the placenta.

(4) In five per cent of human gestations the blastocyst erodes still deeper into the decidua so that the placental area remains at more than one half and up to three fourths of the blastocyst wall. When this fills the uterine cavity at approximately two months of gestation, the placenta then covers a like, tremendous area of the uterine cavity. The increase in volume of the contents (fetus plus amniotic fluid) of the blastocyst causes the small area of fetal membranes to herniate out of the placental cavity so that the placental rim of this cavity is detached from the uterine wall and is eventually pressed back against the marginal face of the remaining discoid placenta. Thus is created placenta circumvallata. Among these the decidual hemorrhage is such that 4 out of 5 abort, and the incidence of placenta circumvallata at term is about one per cent of human gestations.

Since placenta marginata and placenta circumvallata are associated with excess area of early uterine placentation, the marginal excess is reduced with growth during gestation by the disruption of the marginal villi from the decidual bed. This is associated with a varied amount of decidual bleeding. Spontaneous abortion, early, or premature separation of the placenta, late in gestation, are common to these placental anomalies and in reverse order.

Most Breus (subchorial hematoma) moles result from delayed abortion in placenta circumvallata.

With placenta circumvallata, the small area of fetal membranes, on distension, may rupture and the fetus may emerge and continue to live in the naked uterine cavity. This is known as extra-membranous pregnancy, of which there have been approximately 100 instances recorded.

161

(5) On very rare occasions the blastocyst implants still deeper in the decidua and the whole blastocyst surface remains as vascularized placenta. When the blastocyst fills the uterine cavity, the diffuse placenta is known as placenta membranacea. Most of these abort and in the process may create a retained Breus Mole. A few continue into the third trimster of gestation with serious hemorrhage in the neighborhood. There is only one record of a live and healthy infant recovered from this situation.

It is here suggested that this extramembranous mode of placentation without clinical manifestations may occur as the usual condition in the South American Sloths in which there is a simplex uterus lined by decidua.

Approximately 92 per cent of human gestations occur as above described. In the additional 8 per cent of human gestations the blastocyst implants mesometrially into the decidua at the crease or sulcus made by the lateral or apical reflection of the two, ventral and dorsal, sheets of decidua, one to the other. This produces a placenta biloba with one portion on the ventral wall and the other connected portion on the opposite dorsal wall. If the blastocyst implants near to but not in the crease or sulcus, there occurs placenta succenturiata with one or two accesory disks always on the opposite wall of the simplex uterus.

Upwards of ten or twelve per cent of human gestations abort spontaneously. For the great majority these are associated with early gestation, excess placental area resulting in placenta marginata or placenta circumvallata.

In the neighborhood of one per two hundred human gestations the egg is fertilized and the blastocyst forms and is implanted outside of the uterine cavity usually along the fallopian tube canal. This is known as ectopic pregnancy and many times has proved fatal

162

to the mother from internal hemorrhage prior to introduction of surgical operative treatment about a hundred years ago. Very rarely the human egg may become fertilized while it still is in the ovarian follicle, as in certain Cyprinodont fishes, studied by C. L. Turner. In the human female maturation of the embryo-fetus in the ovary becomes an extraordinary form of ectopic pregnancy.

Occasionally the human blastocyst implants in the mucosa low in the uterine cavity. The resulting placenta lies low in the lower uterine segment near the cervix. Expansion of this portion of the uterus as gestation advances may cause disruption of the lower margin of the placenta resulting in sudden bleeding in the third trimester of pregnancy. This alarming situation is known as placenta previa.

In both pathological situations, premature separation of the normally implanted placenta and in placenta previa, the bleeding results from the tendency of the distended uterine wall to slide off of the margin of the placenta. Artificial rupture of the fetal membranes allows release of the amniotic fluid and at the same time abates the tension at the placental edge usually with cessation of further hemorrhage. During the past hundred years this procedure was the time honored treatment.

MULTIPLE SIMULTANEOUS GESTATIONS

In the viviparous reptiles the blastocysts are spaced along the two linear tubular uteri, each in its own dilated lumenal segment. In the marsupials there occurs a marked departure from that in the reptiles. Here the two distinct uteri are truly didelphic for reasons stated elsewhere. In the opossum each uterus has a single large cavity which is filled with highly vascularized folds of the lining mucosa. Into each of these cavities from the ovary, presumably on the same side, are deposited up to ten or more eggs, each about

3/4 mm in diameter. There is far less yolk in these tiny eggs than occurred in the eggs of any previous animal in the evolutionary scale but still far more than in any allantoic placental eutherian mammalian egg. These facts demonstrate the ability of the extraembryonic membranes, including the various sequential placentas, to nourish the growing embryo from very early in gestation. During gestation the ten or more eggs in each uterus of the opossum enlarge to nearly a centimeter each in diameter. Birth at early fetal stage takes place through a passage directly from the uterine exits into the apex of the urogenital sinus and not through the vaginas on either side, which are narrow and distorted by the necessity to extend from the apex of the urogenital sinus around the ureter on each side, both of which pass downward between the Muellerian ducts.

This situation must have been corrected in the eutherian mammals, all of which have a definitive allantoic placenta.

In all eutherian mammals with separate uterine horns and with multiple simultaneous gestations the blastocysts are, as in reptiles, spaced along one of the two linear horns of the uterus, which in these mammals are joined near enough to the common cervix to have at least a short uterine body. When the number of gestation sacs at each pregnancy was reduced to one or two, the linear uterine horns generally became short and stubby.

In that group of eutherian mammals whose placentation is most like that of the ancestral allantoic placental, viviparous reptiles, there are several members which give birth to only one or rarely two newborn. Included in these are the horses (Equidae) and the whales (Cetacea). The allantoic placenta is diffuse, epitheliochorial and without much attachment to the overlying uterine mucosa. Oxygen and subsistence are obtained from uterine secretions. Now, in these two mammals the uterine horns are short and stubby, and the enlarging blastocyst has a tendency to dilate its own uterine horn and to slip down into the cavity of the body of the uterus; the gestation sac also may dilate the uterine opening of the opposite horn and somewhat herniate into it. This condition very likely also may occur in other single infant gestations of the other members of what is here considered to be the first level of eutherian mammals with placentation almost identical to that of the ancestral allantoic placental viviparous reptiles. These mammals are the hippopotamuses, the rhinorceroses and possibly the lemurs, all with one or two fetuses.

Belonging to this group of epitheliochorial eutherian mammals also is the pig (Suidae), which may have multiple births up to 20 or more. As in the viviparous reptiles the blastocysts are spaced along the cavities of the two linear uterine horns. The blastocysts of the pig are long spindle-shaped possibly overlying one another, but in a wrinkled state. Heuser, 1927, stated that if extended to full length, the blastocyst may reach the astonishing length of 30 cm. The embryo develops in the middle, and the two distal ends of the blastocyst tend to atrophy.

This unique conformation of the blastocyst is not known to occur in any other mammal. Apparently this was not inherited from the viviparous reptiles. A. J. Waters, M.D., who compiled a thesis in respect to certain physiological features of the garter snake informed me that the births occur with the coiled fetus still in an oblong capsule with a thin membrane covering. This membrane soon dries in the air and movements of the newborn ruptures it to freedom. Weekes, 1935, illustrated a near term blastocyst of the Australian copperhead viviparous snake, *Denisona suta*. The blastocyst was oval shaped and the fetus therein was coiled like a spring.

In Artiodactyla with one or two fetuses the uterine horns are short. In carnivores, rodents and insectivores with multiple gestations, as a rule, the uterine horns are long and slender to allow spacing of the blastocysts, one below another, so that as in the dog the two term-pregnant uterine cornua in contour are in the shape of link sausages. Some insectivores and almost all of the bats reduced the number of young to one (or sometimes 2), and thus the uterine cornua became short and stubby and finally in the bats the uterine horns disappeared into a simplex uterus. There is no record of this orderly step by step occurrence in any other group of eutherian mammals. Thus it is concluded that the bats first originated the simplex uterus. This accomplishment is such a major event in eutherian mammalian reproduction that the conclusion is inescapable that all such simplex uterine mammals, armadillos, Central American sloths and anteaters, marmosets, monkeys, apes and human beings have received their simplex uterus from the phyllostomid bats.

All of these simplex uterine mammals, with a rather spacious, integral, potential uterine cavity, usually mature one blastocyst, occasionally two, rarely more. The blastocyst implants locally in the uterine deciduous mucosal wall, partially or completely interstitially. The armadillo is recorded as implanting one blastocyst in which develop 4, 8 or 12 embryos, all of the same sex and each with its own amniotic sac, all within the same chorion. The marmoset usually implants one blastocyst in which twins of the same sex occur. The blastocyst is implanted between the ventral and dorsal sheets of decidua into both walls so that the primarily diffuse placenta with growth becomes two discoid placentas with fetal blood vessels traversing the non-placental chorion between them. Many monkeys, especially new world monkeys, have the same type of blastocyst implantation, thus having two placentas, primary and secondary, but with one fetus. Once in a thousand human gestations the same situation occurs resulting in two placentas with one fetus, placenta duplex.

MULTIPLE HUMAN BIRTHS

There are two types of twins or multiple births. The more common of the two results from two fertilized eggs, each of which implants in the simplex uterine cavity with separate placentas. In the human uterus, this may be on the same anterior or posterior wall, one above the other, or side by side or one on the anterior wall and the other on the posterior wall. The resulting infants may or may not be of the same sex and may resemble each other as any other two siblings. Gondotropin hormones, ovary stimulating chemicals produce this type of twinning or of births of more than two up to the not infrequently reported quintuplets or sextuplets.

The other type of twinning, far less common, results from the same egg which separates into two parts, each part developing into an individual embryo. Now, it is possible for one of these to create an embryo while the other portion again divides and its two divisions may originate two more embryos. Thus there may be triplets all resulting from a single egg and all of the same sex having marked resemblance to each other. The common armadillo in the southern part of the United States, and in Central and South America, has an egg which divides into four parts originating four embryos, each in its own amniotic cavity but all four in the same blastocyst. Thus, if all survive, there are four more or less identical individuals of the same sex. There is an armadillo in South America which produces up to 12 fetuses of the same sex.

Ordinarily each such twin or member of a single blastocyst multiple birth resides in its own amniotic sac. In the human female rarely have been reported

167

twins both of which were in the same amnionic sac, as well as in the same blastocyst. Of the nearly 200 case reports only about one third of these survived. In most of those which failed to survive the two umbilical cords had become twisted one around the other causing death by interruption of the fetal circulation.

An interesting book on the study of identical human twins was written by Newman, Freeman and Helzinger, 1937.

The embryological situations described above may occur only in eutherian mammals with a single (simplex) uterus such as is present in phyllostomid bats, African giant water shrews, armadillos, sloths and anteaters, marmosets, monkeys, apes and the human female. In all other eutherian mammals the uterus has a relatively small body but two horns projecting above it. The gestations occur in the cavity of one of the two horns (cornua) and not in the body. Multiple births occur from embryos located at various levels along these two horns. On the other hand marsupials have two distinct uteri, side by side, and at least in the opossum all gestations take place in the common cavity of one of these two uteri. Opossums may have ten or more embryos in each cavity. Among the subsequently evolved eutherian mammals this situation where all gestations were in the body of the uterus did not appear until the final evolution of the primates with a simplex uterus with an expanded uterine cavity.

Thus the early eutherian mammals did not adopt the marsupial method of gestation but did adopt that of the main evolutionary line of the viviparous reptiles which had distribution of the gestation sacs along two uterine horns.

PREDOMINANCE OF RIGHT OR LEFT
SIDE IN REPRODUCTION

It is well known that birds, except predacious birds, have development of the left ovary and oviduct only. Since a similar situation exists in the monotremes, it is only logical to suspect that a similar one also may have occurred in some of the amniote reptiles from which these two warm blooded groups evolved.

Claire Weekes, forty years ago, investigated the reproduction in upwards of 20 Scincid lizards and a few snakes. While her studies were directed toward the uterus and contents, she occasionally mentioned the ovaries, which in each case appeared to be bilaterally equal in development, as were the oviducts. She did note that when the number of gestations bilaterally was equal, the same number occurred in each of the two uteri (oviducts). But when the number was odd the extra fetus almost invariably occurred in the right oviduct. She indicated that this may be due to the enlarged stomach which pressed on the left ovary.

Presumably, oviparous fish have equally developed bilateral ovaries. In the few ovarian-viviparous fish the ovary is single and median. But in sharks there occurs a great deal of variation. Budker, 1971, stated that the ovary in sharks usually is a double organ, but in some species the left ovary atrophies in the adult, and only the right ovary completes its development. Springer, 1948, in reference to the sand shark, *Carcharias taurus,* noted that there was a single functional ovary (right) of a larger adult, which contained an estimated 100 eggs, all about 10 mm in diameter. The volume of the ovary was about 48 ounces. In another specimen only the right ovary was functional but both oviducts were functional. In this specimen there was estimated to be 24,000 eggs varying in diameter from 1 mm to 8 mm. The ovarian mass almost filled a ten quart bucket. These were viviparous, and when the yolk for nutrition was exhausted the embryos devoured subsequently ovarian produced eggs which entered the oviducts.

Metten, 1939, in several diagrams illustrated the single median ovary of the oviparous dogfish. *Scylliorhynus canicula,* and stated that it was believed to be that of the right side.

Springer, 1960-1962, described reproduction in the sandbar shark, *Eulamia milberti.* The adults are six or seven feet long and weigh 115 to 145 pounds, with the females being the larger Mating occurs in the Florida waters in spring or early summer. There is a single large functional ovary, but both oviducts are functional. The eggs are 1 to 1¼ inches in diameter, and after internal fertilization they enter one of the two oviducts, where the shell gland covers them with a diaphanous tube-like shell capable of great expansion to accommodate the growth of the embryo. On an average five eggs, each in the center of its 120 cm long tubular egg case, mature in each oviduct. When the embryos are near maturity, at a length of 24 inches, the vascularized but yolk-empty yolk-sac extends outside of the egg case and presumably obtains water, nutrition and oxygen from uterine secretions. This is a sort of non-invasive yolk-sac placenta, and somewhat similar to that of some viviparous, bilaterally symmetrical invertebrates. Scrimshaw, 1944, state that *Heterandria formosa* as in all poeciliid fishes, the embryos are retained until parturition within the follicles of the single median ovary, the fillicular membrane being referred to as the ovisac. This species is remarkable in showing a high degree of superfetation. As many as eight broods of developing embryos occur within the ovary of a single female. Active sperms are retained in the ovary for many months following a single copulation.

In a summary of her ten years of study of nearly a

score of viviparous reptilian reproductions. Weekes, 1935, stated that the female reproductive organs consist of a right and left ovary equally well developed and a right and left oviduct each opening separately into the cloaca.

Boyd, 1942, indicated that there are paired ovaries as well as paired oviducts in the viviparous gecko, *Hoplodactylus maculatus,* found in New Zealand.

In his study of the placentation in the garter snake, *Thamnophis sirtalis,* Hoffman, 1970, found from 6 to 34 normal embryos per female in four examined, and the right oviduct typically contained more embryos than the left.

Matthews, 1941-44, stated "Most bats, except those of the family Phyllostomidae, have a bicornuate uterus, but nearly always bring forth only one young at birth; consequently, as a rule, only one uterine cornu is occupied by the pregnancy. It has been found in very many species, of different families, that there is a constant tendency for the right side of the genitalia to be the functional one. In many European vespertilionids, although pregnancy can occur on either side, the majority of pregnancies have been found in the right cornu, and in one Rhinolophid bat, (*R. hipposideros minutus*) the present writer has shown that the left ovary appears to be degenerate and never to produce mature ova, the pregnancy being always on the right side (Matthews, 1937a)."

Hartman, 1916-20, demonstrated that both ovaries and both uteri in the opossum are equally developed, each ovary producing a like number of viable eggs and in the two uteri embryos sometimes up to a total of 20 or more, but that there usually are only 13 nipples, rarely 14.

Schumann, 1931, collected a total of 742 histories of human ectopic pregnancy. Slightly more were on

171

the left side (375) than on the right side (365). In 4 there was bilateral tubal pregnancy.

In summary, it may be stated that in most fishes both ovaries and both oviducts develop to function. In some sharks and in those few viviparous fishes both oviducts but only one ovary develop, and this is considered to be from the right side. In birds, as a rule, only the left ovary and left oviduct develop. In some eutherian mammalian bats, in some series of gestations (Matthews) the right uterine horn contained all of the pregnancies. In the human female there appears to be little differentiation and both sides of the reproductive tract function with possible slight predominance of the right side.

MAMMARY GLAND SITE

All bilaterally symmetrical animals tend to have the principal organs bilaterally paired. This does not hold for the power plant of the circulatory system, the heart being single and more or less central. Nor does it hold for the liver and pancreas which are single outpouching adjuncts to the intestine.

The bilaterally paired mammary glands with outlets in nipples or teats in number roughly corresponding to the number of simultaneous newborn, are limited to the lower abdominal areas in monotremes, where multiple openings allow the milk to soak the skin within the mammary pouch. This milk is lapped up by the single infant, or rarely two or three infants. In marsupials, which possess a marsupial pouch, the nipples are confined to the pouch (the Virginia opossum usually has 13 teats, six in a semicircle on each side and one in the center). The South American marsupial, mouse opossum, *Marmosa*, lacks a pouch. The mammae number 9 to 19 depending on the species and some have pectoral mammae as well as abdominal. In marsupial moles, *Notoryctes*, the female has an abdominal pouch which opens posteriorly and contains two teats. In the male the testes are abdominal and there is no scrotum.

Walker, 1968, stated that in the South American shrew-like, insectivorous marsupial family, Caenolestidae, the females in one genus have four abdominal mammae and another five. The marsupium may be present in the young but is absent in the adult.

The marsupial family, Phalangeridae, (named because of special adaptation of the finger bones to aid in climbing) includes the koalas. There is present a well developed pouch which contains two to four mammae in all seventeen genera and opens forward except in the kaola, in which the pouch opens posteriorly.

The marsupial family, Macropodidae, (large footed) with few exceptions are vegetarian, eating mainly grasses. Some species breed only once a year and some may have delayed implantation. A well developed pouch opens forward and contains four mammae, of which only two usually are functional. This family contains the Kangaroos and Wallabies.

The marsupial family, Peramelidae comprises the bandicoots and is the only marsupial family with an allantoic vascularized addition to the usual yolk sac placenta. Females of the family have a pouch that opens downward and backward. They have six, eight or ten mammae, usually eight and the litter ranges from two to six. The immaturity of the newborn appears to equal that of the marsupials with a simple yolk sac placenta.

The insectivorous or carnivorous marsupial family, Dasyuridae, range from mouse-like insectivorous forms to rats, native cats, Tasmanian devils and Tasmanian wolves. The marsupium, if present, opens posteriorly and often is poorly developed. Females have two to twelve mammae, usually six to eight.

The whale, *Cetacea,* has two large recessed nipples, one on each side of the vulva low in the abdominal wall. The ducts are greatly dilated to retain a large quantity of milk to be rapidly transferred to the young so that it will not be required to remain long under water while nursing. A large pup may weigh a ton at birth and gain three tons in three or four months, all from its mother's milk.

The sow has five or six pairs of mammary glands but may be increased to nine pairs, while the closely allied peccary has only two.

In horses, tapirs and rhinoceroses, the mammae are located in the groin.

In general, the Madagascar lemurs have two to four mammae located on the chest. An exception is the Madagascar aye-aye (Daubentonia) which has two abdominal mammae.

Galagos (African bush babies) like most of the Madagascar lemurs, have a pair of mammary glands situated pectorally.

In the Artiodactyla, grazing mammals, the mammae are located in one or two pairs in the inguinal region and these may be fused into an udder.

The order Hyracoidea consists of one recent family, Procaviidae. The females of the genus, *Heterohyrax,* have one pair of pectoral mammae and two pairs of inguinal mammae.

Shared with the Hyracoidea, the Sirenia and Proboscidea possess an unique type of placentation found in no other mammal. In the manatees and in elephants belonging to these two latter groups the single paired mammae are pectoral in site.

In the females of the order Carnivora, the mammae are variable in number, located on the abdomen, except in ursidae in which the mammae are abdominal and pectoral.

Their mode of placentation supports the concept that the pinnipeds were carnivores that returned to the sea for a livelihood. In general they give birth to one or two pups and have 2 to 4 mammae on the lower abdomen.

The cat generally has four pairs of mammary glands and the bitch four or five.

The rodents include 35 families and 351 genera and 8 extinct families. This order exceeds all others in variety and actual numbers but the fossil record is comparatively poor.

In rodents the mammary glands usually are arranged in two separate groups, a pectoral and an abdominal-inguinal one. The mountain viscacha (related to the chinchilla) has a single pair situated in the pectoral region.

In the rodents, rat, mouse and hamster five to seven pairs of mammae are present but the multi-mammate possesses ten pairs while the quinea pig has only a single inguinal pair.

In the order Insectivora, the females, of the family Solenodontidae, the two mammae are located in the inguinal region. In the females of the family, Tenrecidae, some are very prolific, one genus, *Tenrec*, having up to 25 in a litter. The numerous mammae (*Tenrec* has 12 pairs) are abdominal and possibly also pectoral in location. In hedgehogs the females have five pairs of mammae. In the family Potamogalidae (African water shrews) the females have two mammae situated in the groin region. In the family, Chrysochloridae, (golden moles) the females have one pair of abdominal mammae and one pair of inguinal mammae.

There is a primitive insectivore (*Centetes*) with 22 to 24 nipples and up to 21 young at birth.

Among the insectivores, the Solenodons, the females

have an urogenital sinus, and the rectum is separate as in the marsupials. The two mammae are located in the inguinal region.

Tenrecs (Madagascar hedgehogs) in the family Tenrecidae are in one of the few families of eutherian mammals in which the females possess a cloaca. One genus (*tenrec*) is extremely prolific, having up to 25 young in a litter. Probably the numerous mammae may be abdominal extending upon the thoracic region.

The insectivorous elephant shrews have pectoral teats.

In his *Mammals of the World,* Walker, 1968, devoted 210 pages with more than 200 illustrations to the Chiroptera. He stated that bats, in general, have one young per year. One genus (Lasiurus) of the family, Vespertilionidae has four functional mammae and the number of young of the genus is two to four, usually two or three. Apparently this genus of the vespertilionid family comprises the only bat that has more than one or two young at a time.

Like some bats, the flying lemurs (Dermoptera) carry a single young in flight and the mother has two mammary gland nipples on the chest region toward the arm pits, one on either side.

In the African giant water shrews, the testes in the male are borne in a scrotum, and the females have two mammae located in the groin region.

Some bats have two false teats in the groin region not connected to mammary glands. When the mothers are suspended upside down the infants hang from these teats.

In the Linnaean order of primates all females generally have a pair of mammary glands on the chest. Exceptions are the female tree shrews (Tupaiidae) which have two or three pairs of mammae and the aye-aye (Daubentonia) which has two abdominal mammae. The penis in primates is of the pendulous type which occurs also in bears and bats. The testes are borne in a sac, the scrotum.

Most female mammals with a simplex uterus have a pair of mammae situated in the thoracic region. The African giant water shrew, *Potamogale,* with a pair of inguinal mammae is an exception.

These mammals are Phyllostomid bats, South American Xenarthra (armadillos, sloths and anteaters) marmosets, monkeys, apes and human beings.

The morphology of the genitalia in the male and female mammals has been described adequately in Marshall's *Physiology of Reproduction,* 1960, reprinted from the 3rd edition of 1956.

Information of the mammary gland site was obtained chiefly from Walker's *Mammals of the World,* 1968 and from Marshall's *Physioligy of Reproduction,* 1960.

CURIOSITIES IN ANIMAL REPRODUCTION

The metazoan animals, indigenous to the sea, anamniote invertebrates and early vertebrates alike, reproduced by the female deposition of yolked eggs in water followed by sperms spread over them by the male for fertilization. Some few individuals had both male and female gonads and thus were hermaphroditic.

There was at least one great exception. The vertebrate sharks, oviparous, ovoviviparous or viviparous, all practiced internal fertilization by male female copulation. No penis was present and the male used a hollowed-out pelvic fin rib to introduce into the female cloaca for sperm deposit. Sharks may have only one ovary develop and this is said to be the right ovary, but both oviducts develop to function. In certain birds, of course with amniote, blastocystic eggs, the left ovary only develops and only the left oviduct then functions, the right side of the reproductive apparatus remaining quiescent.

A large, oviparous shark may produce eggs with a quantity of yolk to equal the size of a large orange. To this yolk the ovarian follicle binds a minute quantity of living protoplasm by a thin membrane. The egg must be fertilized by male-female copulation prior to the next step, which occurs in the upper part of the oviduct, where the shell gland covers the egg with an expansible keratinous shell. Not infrequently there are long slender tentacles on the shell case which tend to fix the egg to vegetation in the hatching waters. The incubation of these eggs is very long, up to a year or more, when the infant shark may be nearly two feet long being doubled up in its casing shell. The keratinous shell must be pervious to oxygen and likewise to water and probably to some chemicals dissolved in the water.

Now, some sharks are ovoviviparous, that is, the large yolked egg inside the keratinous shell is retained in one of the two maternal oviducts until it hatches and the fetus is born alive.

Others are truly viviparous in which case the shell is deleted or soon fragmented in the cavity of one of the two uterine horns. In general these eggs are given less yolk. Thus after the yolk is exhausted, how are nourishment, oxygen and water administered to the growing fetus? There have been described three distinct methods. (1) Trophonemous, vascularized strands off of the uterine mucosa extend into the spiracle (nose hole) to the esophagus for nutrition. (2) In some species of viviparous sharks the fetus, after exhausting its supply of yolk, eats and digests subsequently maternal ovarian produced eggs which enter the uterine cavity.

(3) In a few species of viviparous sharks the fetal vascularized yolk-sac, when the yolk is exhausted, may remain and serve as a yolk-sac placenta, lying free in the uterine secretions or, being lightly attached to a trophonemous cup on the wall of the uterus where uterine secretions are directly obtained by the yolk-sac vessels. Oxygen may be secured in this way but oxygen also may be obtained through the fetal skin covering, or by gills. (Sometime in the future, there may be discovered an ovoviviparous shark species in which the intrauterine fetuses cannibalize each other as in the amphibian urodele, *Salamandra atra*).

For the most part, calcareous bony fishes are oviparous. The eggs, being without amnion or blastocyst, and composed of a tiny speck of living protoplasm, membrane-attached to a relatively large supply of yolk (but never approaching that of the sharks) are produced in the ovarian follicles and passed out through the oviducts and cloaca. Generally, these fishes are oviparous with eggs deposited in water where they are fertilized by the male (external fertilization).

There are at least two groups which are viviparous but using different methods. Many of the family Cyprinodontes are small, mosquito larva eating fishes living in high plateau lake or stream water, principally in Mexico and neighboring South America. These may be said to be ovarian viviparous. Male-female copulation similar to that of the sharks fertilizes the eggs while they still are in the follicles of the single median ovary. Here they develop to maturity but in some species the follicles rupture into a common central ovarian cavity where these embryos mature. They are nourished in various fashions quite similar to the unique methods used by the shark fetuses in the uterus after the yolk deposit has been exhausted.

There is another group of viviparous fishes in the family Clinidae, one of 15 families in the suborder Blennioidei of which the other families apparently are oviparous. The Clinidae are said to be orthodox in their viviparity in that, as in sharks, the embryos develop within the maternal reproductive tract and not in the ovaries. Necessary internal fertilization is provided by male-female copulation. The male, as in sharks, makes use of a hollowed anal fin rib to introduce sperms into the female cloaca.

In 1944-45, Frederic Wood Jones described some reproductive curiosities in mammals. In at least two eutherian mammals the urethra in the female is buried within and traverses the length of the clitoris. Thus the enlarged clitoris has the appearance of the male penis and differentiation of the sexes by casual observation is impossible except by an expert who is able to observe members of the opposite sex at the same time for minute inspection of slight differences. These mammals are the spotted hyena, *Crocuta crocuta*, (two other species have conventional genitalia) and the European mole, *Talpa europa*. This situation was very puzzling and the love life of the spotted hyena figured in ancient literature.

In the spotted hyena copulation must consist of approximation of the tip of the penis to that of the clitoris for transfer of sperms. Parturition takes place only through the urethra in the clitoris just as the semen in the male only exists through the penile urethra.

The European mole has a perineal anatomy in the female similar to that of the spotted hyena but in the mole insemination and parturition do not occur through the urethra in the enlarged clitoris. When the female mole is beginning the second year of life, marked congestion occurs in the perineal region and a new opening appears between the anus and the base of the clitoris. This aperture extends to the urogenital sinus and becomes a temporary vagina for copulation and parturition, following which this opening again closes and the tissues grow together until the next spring of the year when the process is repeated.

The experiences of the marsupials, of the spotted hyena and of the European mole demonstrate a relative law of biology. When in the course of genetic mutations a heritable anatomic deviation appears, there are only two courses to follow, to give up and become extinct or to adapt the anomaly to functional survival. For possibly 200 million years the marsupial survived, burdened with a very complex method of parturition. Sometime in the past 60 million years originated the bizarre perineal anatomy of the European moles and of the spotted hyena. As was suggested by Jones, the laughing hyena has a perfect right to laugh.

Jones recorded other curiosities in respect to the sperms in invertebrates. The queen bee, on her nuptial flight, receives from the drone an estimated 4 to 25 million sperms which may remain active for 5 years. She may lay 2,000 eggs per day and she still retains the power to produce from one to one and a half million fertile eggs during the rest of her life. Since she mates only once these sperms must remain viable.

Long retention of viable sperms is more common in the invertebrates but may occur in some vertebrates. Jones noted that many male bats became sexually active early in the fall of the year when they inseminate the females. The sperms are bound in a large quantity of mucus which becomes more or less a solid plug in the female reproductive tract. The female becomes reproductively active in the following spring when ovulation occurs and fertilization from the stored sperms initiates gestation.

In the primitive multiple celled animals there was one common exit for gut waste products, products of gestation and for kidney excretions in urine. This situation existed in invertebrates, sharks, fishes, amphibians, reptiles, birds and monotremes. In Marsupials the cloaca was separated into two tubular exits, the posterior rectum for gut wastes and the separate anterior urogenital sinus for reproduction and urination in both males and females.

In the eutherian mammals, in general, in the female there was further separation of the urogenital sinus into vagina and urethra both of which with some exceptions opened on the perineum. In the marsupial and in the eutherian males there is a separate rectal exit and a common one for sperms and urine, and there has been no change in this situation since its first use in the marsupials, or in possibly some antecedent reptiles.

The female opossum like all other marsupials, has a single urogenital sinus which is used by the male for introduction of the penis for copulation. The female marsupials have two uteri and two vaginas, the latter of which open separately into the apex of the urogenital sinus. The male has an erectile, muscular penis split at the distal end so that each half serves one of the two vaginas at the top of the urogenital sinus.

Some invertebrates and some vertebrates living in the sea or lakes have skin pouches on the body of the female or male for deposition of the eggs which are fertilized there to mature. In the sea horses and in the pipe fishes these are on the males.

Of the sea-indigenous metazoan, vertebrate animals almost all reproduce by the female depositing eggs in water where the male spreads sperms over them for fertilization. There is one great exception. All sharks, rays and skates employ male female copulation whereby a hollowed-out rib of a pelvic fin is used to introduce into the female cloaca for insemination. There also is a minor exception. All of the few viviparous fishes, of necessity, must practice male female copulation.

Sharks, which may have large-yolked anamniote

eggs, may have only one ovary develop. Thus in sharks, or in some ovarian-viviparous fishes, the only ovary that develops is said to be the right ovary. Birds, on the other hand, with large yolked, amniote (blastocystic) eggs develop only the left ovary and left oviduct. In the shark with one ovary both oviducts develop.

Possibly one in ten thousand human females has two vaginas, side by side. There is no evolutionary stage other than in the marsupials in which this situation exists, the rule being a single median vent, a cloaca in fishes, amphibians and the ancestral reptiles. The two vaginas in the marsupials do not extend to the outside but first open into a single urogential sinus which leads outside.

The invertebrates on land evolved numerous ingenious methods of protecting the eggs and feeding the larva. These ranged from complete exposure to burial in vegetation or deep in the trunk of a tree, to incubation within the body of a living host. In the latter instances, in some, to complete the cycle, stages were required to be transferred to successive hosts often of entirely different family or species.

Some catfish males (or females) collect the fertilized eggs in the mouth where they are held during incubation. Such practices and other odd modes of egg incubation were not uncommon in the amphibians.

Among the invertebrate Arachnids there is said to be a female spider of such a mean disposition that if a male comes near enough to touch her she grabs him, kills him and eats his body. Consequently the male approaches just out of range, deposits his sperms and then leaves. The female then picks up the sperms by her cloaca.

In some species of the Praying Mantis during copulation the male may not be able to eject the sperms until the female has eaten his head off. Being a devoted helpmate he contributes not only sperms but food as well.

The following curiosity may have little to do with reproduction but it occurs only in the male. The male monotreme has a cornified spur on each hind leg above the ankle. Since these mammals are not too far distant from birds, this spur may be homologous to that occurring above the ankles on male birds.

According to Herald, 1962, the grunion, *Leuresthes tenuis*, is a member of the Silversides family of fishes and inhabits the shores of Southern and Lower California. It has striking spawning habits high on the beach at night during the period of the highest tides. The female wriggles into the sand where the eggs are buried at a depth of two inches while the male wraps himself around her for external fertilization of the eggs. Immediately the mating pair separate and each flops back into the water and thus carried out to sea. The eggs incubate and the sea water of the next high tide triggers hatching. Spawning time is correlated to the phases of the moon, occurring a day or two after each full or new moon.

Apparently whales and horses were very closely related in placentation and the genitalia of a whale are very similar to those of a horse. Sir William Turner, an eminent anatomist of Edinburgh, in 1870, described the anatomy, with special reference to reproduction, in a 78 foot Finner Whale (Balaenoptera sibbaldii), estimated to weigh 74 tons. She was near full term in pregnancy with the fetus measuring 19 feet long and estimated to weigh half a ton. The mother became stranded on the rocks near Longuiddry and was towed ten miles to a beach where it was found that her uterus had been ruptured. The fetus lay head up toward the mother's head and it is now known that the method of delivery is by breech.

The female genital organs are similar to those of a

mare whose mammary glands are nearby on the abdomen between the thighs. The nipples in this whale were recessed in pockets one on either side of the vulva. The milk ducts were engorged up to four inches in diameter to allow the submerged infant to quickly fill its stomach so that it can come to the surface for air. The vagina was measured to be six feet long. This means that the corresponding male penis must have been similar to that of a super giant stallion.

WEIGHT OF THE MOTHER TO THAT OF THE FETUS

In respect to the comparative weights of the mother and her newborn, in his superb monograph on "Possums", Hartman, 1952, presented data summarized as follows. Among eutherian mammals the human female weighs 16 to 29 times as much as her newborn infant. The Molossid bat, *Nyctinomus mexicanus* may deliver an infant one third of the mother's weight. A bear may weigh 300 to 700 times as much as her newborn infant whose birth occurs during the winter sleep usually in a cave. The extreme reduction in size of the newborn is illustrated in the marsupials where the birth occurs in the early fetal stage. An opossum female may weigh 8,000 times as much as her offspring at birth while a kangaroo may be 60,000 times heavier than the joey at birth.

DEVELOPMENT OF THE BRAIN

A brain essentially is a computer, a marvelous and compact one at that. The vertebrate brain began with the most primitive fish and evolved through the fishes, amphibians, reptiles to mammals, and each group in this series benefited by inheritance from the previous groups. The evolution proceeded in a slow and orderly fashion. When genetic probing propelled a species into a new situation, there were only two avenues open; one to give up and become extinct, the other to overcome the difficulty in any of many ways that further genetic probing could devise. Those in the new situation, if they survived, found new aspects of the ecology to exploit.

All along this way some species were stranded because their particular ecology remained plentiful and constant. The sharks, possibly half a billion years old, were such, and they survived without necessity to change. Once evolved and established in a species the mode of reproduction could not be altered, and there was no need to improve brains nor their morphology except to streamline the latter.

Man has the rather egotistical idea that his brain is far superior to that of other animals. That may be very true in respect to understanding his environmental phenomena and in putting these to his own use and in ability to conceive of abstract concepts. However, it is equally true that all other mammals and all reptiles, not to mention their ancestors, had brains that were equally efficient for survival.

Furthermore these primitive brains collected information from sense organs highly developed for survival in their particular ecology. A snake slithering through the underbrush is perfectly aware of its immediate surroundings. The brain receives sensation through vibrations in the ground or possibly in the air. It receives and distinguishes minute changes in temperature and can judge the direction of the source and size of the object. With its acutely sensitive tongue it can taste extraneous atoms in the air. All these sensory imputs received by the brain are almost instantly transplanted into action, whether, to attack unerringly for food or defense, to pass on or to turn tail and run away. Mammals inherited a brain which had hundreds of millions of years in evolution and perfection. It is likewise true that mammals evolved specialized brains emphasizing certain sensation receiving organs such as visual, olfactory and auditory, allowing others such as perception of vibrations to become less sensitive. There were exceptions in those that returned to the sea, porpoises, whales, manatees, and the carnivorous sea-living mammals. Those that took to the air, bats, also were exceptions. They even amplified vibration sensations in the development of Echolocation, the rudiments of which they probably inherited from the reptiles. Mammals, traveling on four extremities or on two in an upright position, true bipeds, or in flight as in bats, required a brain highly developed in control of muscular coordination and body weight balance.

All members of the human race realize that they possess intelligence superior to that of their reluctantly acknowledged distant cousins, monkeys and apes. Few ever have understood the process by which this became so, and seldom have they aired their views on the subject. Now there must have been a reason, probably very simple, which extended over tremendous periods of time.

In the past several decades I have given this subject considerable mental reflection, mulling over many probabilities or possibilities. The most simple and yet logical line of reasoning follows. Our direct ancestors, probably from the early branching off from the main stem of eutherian mammalian evolution, were mainly tree climbers where they lived. This mode of life produced two morphological attributes (1) the evolution of the thumb (and big toe) as grasping digits in conjunction with the other four digits on each extremity. (Pentadactylism dates back into the remote reptilian ancestry). (2) the position of the eyes evolved from the sides of the head to the plane of the face where bifocal vision became possible and was essential in judging distance in leaping from branch to branch. Likewise a depth of focus from distant to near was evolved.

The most important fact of our ancestors' sojourn

in the trees was that this mode of life was terminated at just the right time prior to the loss of the opposability of the thumb to the other digits. Had they remained in the trees longer (as happened to some other primates), the thumb would have begun to atrophy in favor of a hook-like hand used in brachiation. The descent from the trees possibly was forced by recession of the rain forest. At any rate, human ancestors moved to the ground equipped with a fairly good range of bifocal vision and at least a grasping thumb in the hand. On the ground there took place the prolonged evolution of the plantigrade foot.

An interesting point is how they proceeded from there to present day civilization in a relatively short period of time, possibly 2,000,000 years. The principal two attributes possessed by modern man and not by his distant ancestors were (1) an increase in range of visual focus from infinity to almost microscopic and in the latter category objects not much more than a tenth of a millimeter in diameter ,(2) a remarkable ability to manipulate the thumb in conjunction with the other four digits.

In order to develop these two refinements there must have been constant daily practice by all members of the family with this activity proceeding over hundreds of thousands of years. The only possible situation to force this sort of activity must have been as follows. When the primitive primates moved to the ground their hairy coats must have become a haven for all sorts of insect vermin. The irritation and itching caused by these insects compelled measures of relief. A dog can respond only by scratching, but these primates had adequate eyesight and maneuverable fingers to part the hair and seek out the particular offending insect. Judging from observation of non-human primates, this so-called grooming activity practiced on each other may have involved many hours each day of individuals of both sexes and of all ages from infancy

Fig. 24.—Trees and Fleas.

to old age. By this process the eyes gradually became able to focus on closer and closer objects smaller and smaller in diameter. Likewise, the manipulation of the thumb in conjunction with the opposing digits became more and more intricate and precise.

These two attributes of the human ancestors, maintained and improved by constant practice induced by the ever present irritating arthropods, gave them all of the physical equipment required in modern civilization long before they put them to full use. Thus, the ability to make use of mechanical invention was present long before the latter arrived.

Primitive invention was primarily accidental occurring first to one individual and adopted by other observers to be put into general use depending upon its immediate value. Possibly the use of tools began when two males were at their common occupation of fighting each other. One may have been knocked down but came up accidently clutching a rock or club which he used on his opponent, winning the bout. The observers recognized the value of the new weapon and adopted it. They thus became the supreme group until the other groups learned the same lesson. The individual who attached a bone or wooden handle to a rock to make a hammer was truly an Einstein of his day. Goodall showed that our nearest cousins, the chimpanzees do not use rocks as weapons but do possess a tool of sorts. A slender branch or straw is employed by inserting it into an ant hill. When withdrawn it is covered with ants which are then eaten.

Civilization rests upon only a few fundamental concepts, possibly thirty. I suspect that the female mind originated the first three. The first one, monogamy, possibly occurred in some such fashion. Prior to this, males and females in families grouped together. When a female became in heat all of the available males, the strongest first, had sexual intercourse with her. Possibly some Cleopatra of her day sat upon a fallen tree trunk and reasoned thus. "If I could submit to sexual intercourse any day on demand instead of a few days a month I could secure one of these handsome lords for my exclusive use". This she proceeded to do, and when she had secured him, she took him away from the group to start a family of her own. She wished to get away from the other females, and he was anxious for adventure. Such may have been the origin of monogamy, the first fundamental practice on the way to civilization. Now, in their new home she probably tended the site while he roamed, hunting in the woods and plains. She may have found a plant on the hillside not growing well, but when she moved it nearer to the stream, it grew better. She thus became the mother of agriculture and the second invention toward civilization. Likewise, he or she discovered a newborn wolf, goat or sheep and took it to camp where most likely she fed, nursed and trained it. She thus became the mother of animal husbandry, the third fundamental concept. She then sat herself down and decided that in the future the female mind, in general, would devote its energies to training animals, husbands and offspring. Almost all subsequent inventions probably were made by males, however, often in honor of some hypothetical, composite female involving his mother, his wife or sweetheart. Chemistry evolved from control of fire. Numbers to denote quantity and words to denote ideas evolved from property rights either in live stock, grains, parcels of land or in media of exchange. Possibly the female had the principal part in evolution of weaving.

Man in general delegated tasks requiring constant attention and patience to his female counterpart or to children. Eighty years of observation has brought me to the conclusion that, as a rule, when a woman has secured a man and legally bound him as a husband, no matter what a paragon he may be, he never is perfect in her sight. She immediately begins to make him over better to her liking. It also is true that the majority of women perform this operation with so much innate adroitness and finesse that individually the husband may never suspect what is happening to him. She even may convince him that he originated the performance. All in all, one must admit that the system has worked reasonably well notwithstanding the fact that man by inheritance is a promiscuous animal.

LOWER MAMMAL BASIS FOR THE HUMAN BRAIN

As already noted the whole eutherian line possessed in common most of the bones, muscles, skin, nerves and internal organs with similar functions including the brain. Futhermore, the evolution of this entire line, from beginning to end, occurred in a phenomenally short period of time, possibly 10 million years. Now the question arises as to which of these lower mammals

191

possessed the imaginative and inventive type of brain worthy of being the foundation for the human brain.

Among members of the first level above the ancestral viviparous reptiles there are exhibited some very adaptable brains. The porpoise recently has received much attention. It lived a communal life in sea water. Therefore, it was obliged to evolve a communication system which consisted of intelligible sound waves in water. In the case of the dolphins, porpoises and whales, this involved a considerable vocabulary. In the same first level, pigs and horses readily became domesticated by man who provided a good living and a protected life. In the case of the pigs and horses this involved a trade. For a relatively luxurious life from infancy to adulthood the pig offered his carcass after death. The horse traded his labor, very useful to man, for adequate food and protection against climate and enemies in the wild state.

In the next level cows and sheep and others made a similar deal with man. In addition cows gave milk and sheep, wool. So it goes up the line. Wild dogs, as was early man, were predatory hunters, so it was natural that they pool their proclivities not only to obtain food but to satisfy an inborn instinct of the most pleasant variety. Tamed dogs then became useful to man in protecting his property consisting of home and a variety of live stock. Dogs became fast and warm personal friends of man. Cats, on the other hand, likewise domesticated to rid the neighborhood of pesky rodents, in general appeared to have a superior, condescending attitude, which appealed to the independent spirit of man.

When an ecology once was chosen, most mammals exploited their own particular niche, and few exhibited any great degree of ingenuity. However, there was one exception. Probably originated as insectivores, the bats must have noted that their prospective meal took off with wings and flew out of danger. Thus, they tediously elaborated their bodies into flying machines and took after the flying insects or arthropods. In daylight they had competition with birds, and since insects flew more at night, the bats invented an echolocation system of catching them in total darkness.

The bats had still more surprises. Some tend to augment their insectivorous diet with ripening fruit. Some catch small birds on the wing. Some species in South America fly over water and by their clawed feet grab out a top minnow. The most amazing of all bat ecologies is that of the vampire bats, which borrowed from the distant invertebrates a technique of utilizing blood drawn from large vertebrates.

Such practical and complicated inventions on the part of the bats were indicative of only the most adaptable central nervous system and the only one ever in existence worthy of being the basis of the human central nervous system. The bats probably accomplished these remarkable achievements over a few million years while it has required upwards of 60 million years for man's brain to figure out how they did it and then to create machines to emulate their performances.

The position of the bats in the evolutionary scale leading to man was enhanced by their sole performance in creating the simplex uterus.

ANIMAL LOVING CHILDREN

If you are fortunate enough to be the proud parent of a child who has an instinctive love of animals please do not discourage this attachment even though you are obliged to put up with turtles, lizards and snakes in your bathtub. The schools, likewise should promote this interest. Supposing each high school biology department incidentally studied the wild animals indigenous to the limited territory round about and encouraged the interested students in collecting specimens, there might be the opportunity to discover and

name a new species. Furthermore, the internal reproductive methods of many animals are unknown. Embryologists in larger colleges, zoological and medical schools, for more than a hundred years have investigated the internal reproductive processes of a wide range of animals. But think of this; these methods of reproduction have been worked out in only about 200 species of eutherian mammals and many of these include a single report. These schools have the personnel and equipment to do much more investigation. The obstacle lies in obtaining the animals in the reproductive seasons. Furthermore, it is very expensive to send out teams of biological experts to chase them down. This process would be much more feasible if done by students of local high schools and colleges the world over where the breeding seasons could better be defined. Such an enterprise would serve as an apprenticeship to young biologists. Much of the previous work has been done by interested individuals, to name a few: Sir William Turner, Duval, van Beneden, Strahl, Assheton, Heape, Grosser, Hubrecht, Hill, Weekes, Wislocki, Gerard, De Lange, Lee, Hartman, Hamlett, Mossman, Streeter, Heuser, Wimsatt, Hertig, Ramsey, Gopalakrishna and many others.

This world is a unit and all life is related to all other life. Animals, often our own very close relatives, have been hunted too frequently to near extinction. We must relinquish the idea that man is apart from the other mammals. All are one great family. It so happens that man alone evolved enough intelligence and auxiliary tools to become the ruler over the earth but this does not mean total annihilation of his cousins. Furthermore, there are many interesting and instructive facts about how they managed to survive 60 million years or more since mammals evolved from reptiles of the prior couple of hundred million years of the Mesozoic era.

For this zoologically gifted child of yours a hundred

dollars could well be spent in securing at least two sets of books. For mammals, the extremely complete *Mammals of the World* by Walker describes and illustrates so many mammals that more than 200 individual species of bats appear, described and illustrated. The recently published *The Encyclopedia if the Animal World* by many biologists describes and color-illustrates all the better known animals including invertebrates and vertebrates. In the latter are fishes, amphibians, reptiles, birds, monotremes, marsupials and eutherian mammals. Authoritative details are presented in a style easily comprehended. There are on the market many other valuable sets of books devoted to the same subject, and relatively complete accounts of almost any animal may be found in one of the two great encyclopedias, *Americana* or *Britannica*. While extensive, the knowledge of embryology is yet in its infancy and the future depends upon these gifted young people whose development in biology too often has been aborted.

EMBRYOLOGY TEACHING FOR MEDICAL STUDENTS

Of all groups of individuals, physicians should have received at least a basic knowledge of embryology. Experience leads to the belief that few have been so exposed.

In the course in embryology which particular one probably ranked high among those presented anywhere in 1914, the chief work was upon the chick embryo and consisted of many drawings of microscopic sections and with very little understanding of the overall picture. As I remember, those artistic individuals who made the best pictures received the highest grades. The rest of us for the most part passed.

Since the course for the incipient M.D. is relatively short it seems that the instruction should include much work with at least three colors of modeling clay. The microscope should be used in conjunction but rather sparingly. In the short time available the student should obtain basic knowledge of anamniote eggs of three varieties; oviparous, ovoviviparous and viviparous. Of course these would be limited to invertebrates, fishes, sharks and amphibians. Basic knowledge also should include the three varieties of amniote (blastocyst) eggs; oviparous, ovoviviparous and viviparous common to reptiles and, their descendants.

The egg blastocyst is oviparous in many reptiles, all birds and in monotremes. The blastocyst is ovoviviparous in some reptiles and since in monotremes much of the egg maturation occurs in the maternal reproductive tract this primitive mammal might be considered to be sub-ovoviviparous. True viviparity occurs in some reptiles with yolk-sac mesodermic vascularization of the trophoblast from which stage originated the marsupials, and in some, more evolved, reptiles with allantoic vascularization of the trophoblast from which originated all eutherian mammals.

The first vertebrate placenta occurred in one of the viviparous (anamniote) sharks. The yolk-sac, on a vascular pedicle and itself highly fetal-vascularized, first consumed its supply of yolk. When this was completed it attached itself as a large cotyledon to a trophonemous cup on the highly vascularized uterine wall mucosa. The connection did not result in epithelial cell loss but more readily supplied the embryo-fetus with nutrition, oxygen and water absorbed from uterine mucosal secretions. This crude mechanism occurred more than 100 million years prior to the placentation associated with the blastocyst.

The trophoblastic covering of the blastocyst, in viviparous reptiles became fetal vascularized either by yolk-sac mesodermic vessels or by allantoic sac mesodermic vessels. The first of these two was by yolk-sac vascularization creating an entirely fetal yolk-sac placenta in some viviparous reptiles from which evolved the marsupials whose placenta is composed of yolk-sac vascularized trophoblast obtaining nutrition, water and oxygen from uterine gland secretions. (In perameles there is an additional portion vascularized by the allantoic mesoderm).

The last to form was the allantoic vascularized trophoblastic placenta in some reptiles and from which evolved the most primitive eutherian mammals with an entirely fetal allantoplacenta and still obtaining nutrition, oxygen and water from uterine gland secretions. The blastocyst lay central in a segment of a linear tubular horn of a bicornuate tubular uterus. Subsequently, in additional levels of eutherian mammals, the fetal placenta acquired more and more maternal components principally from deciduous mucosa until, finally, it was able to bury itself in a self-created cavity in uterine wall decidua.

Simultaneously, the number of blastocysts to be maturated was reduced to one or two and the separate uterine horns became shorter and shorter and finally disappeared into the body of a simplex uterus. A study of the pertinent literature reveals that the bats were the only mammals to make an orderly and successful effort to create the simplex uterus.

In the anamniotes there are two methods of insemination of the egg, external, after the eggs are expelled by the female into the surrounding water environment, where the male spreads sperm over them, and internal, which has two varieties (1) packets of sperms known as spermatophores are picked up by the lips of the female cloaca, and (2) internal insemination by male-female copulation.

All amniote (blastocystic) eggs are internally fertilized by male-female copulation. In all instances of both anamniote and amniote procedures sex hormones lay the foundation for the process. In the intervals between the sexual cycles a hungry and voracious anamniote male shark may devour the female.

Employment of molding clay graphically may demonstrate most of the sequential situations in the maturation of either type of eggs, using various colors to illustrate the extraembryonic portions. Certain accessory membranes may be added by use of thin wrapping plastic.

The instruction should include the fact that every eutherian mammalian blastocyst which attaches to the uterine, usually deciduous, mucosa does so in at least two of three consecutive fashions; (1) non-vascularized trophoblast infiltration, (2) yolk-sac entodermal underlying of the trophoblast to create a secondary yolk-sac placenta and (3) allantoic vascularized trophoblast to produce the tertiary, definitive and and henceforth permanent placenta. The first two of these might be referred to as pre-placentas since they are allowed to atrophy and generally to disappear when the allanto-placenta is established.

In the herein postulated eutherian mammalian levels, 1, 2, 7, and 8 the secondary yolk-sac placenta does not appear, since the yolk-sac vessels never reach to the trophoblastic covering of the blastocyst. The primary non-vascularized trophoblast placenta proceeds directly by allantoic vascularization.

EMBRYOLOGICAL EVOLUTION. LIFE ON OTHER PLANETS

Among the myriads of planets in other solar systems that may parallel the evolutionary changes in our own planet many may have evolved primitive life such as had occurred on earth. Now when they came to the halt in life evolution at the full development of the invertebrates and of the early water borne vertebrates sharks, fishes and amphibians, it would be rare indeed for them to have amphibians as smart as ours were in creating a whole new line of animals based upon the blastocyst rather than upon the simple yolked-egg.

Man is and should be very proud of his manned space capsule that allows him to escape from earth's oxygenated atmosphere and to survive in the vacuum of outer space. However, this is a replica of the first manned space capsule, invented by the amphibians without any blueprints of previous experience which allowed the amphibian descendants to leave the sea entirely and to colonize the land masses.

An interesting point about their accomplishment was that it had to be done in sequences and failure meant that there would be no more chances to go back and repeat it.

LIFE ON OTHER PLANETS

One thing is quite certain, life on any planet in any other solar system must proceed or must have proceeded in exactly the same step by step fashion exhibited by the animals on this planet. As demonstrated here each step leads to another step and in the process there were many pitfalls that had to be avoided. Many of these would have proved fatal to the line, especially failure of the phenomenal amphibians in creating the incomparable blastocyst, absolutely necessary for establishment of a colonization of the land masses. According to reliable estimates, on our own planet there was the following time-table. Life in the non-nucleated, prokaryote, cell began some 3 billion years ago. It required 2 billion years to add a nucleus to this blob of living protoplasm to form the eukaryote cell. Along with the nucleus came bisexualism. Another 300 million years intervened before the animal nucleated cell was originated from former nucleated plant cells. The plant cell could synthesize its own nutrition but this feature was not granted to the animal cell, which then was obliged to consume plant cells for essential amino-acids. Another 350 million years was necessary to create the invertebrates and primitive vertebrates. These latter came on land to colonize it about 350 million years ago.

The reptiles inherited the blastocyst from the amphibians and they required some 200 million years to evolve viviparity in the yolk-sac vessel vascularized trophoblastic placenta. Many more millions of years were spent in evolving the allantoic vascularized placenta which, about 70 to 60 million years ago was presented to the eutherian line of mammals. These, in possibly the short time of 10 million years, completed the transformation of the blastocyst site from existence free in the uterine lumen to ability to bury itself in a new cavity within the uterine mucosal wall.

The earthly eutherian mammals inherited from the reptiles a bicornuate uterus with the gestations occurring in the lumen of one or both horns. In the final stage of this evolution, the two horns were shortened and finally disappeared in the simplex uterus as in the human female.

The simplex uterus was characteristic of the final level of eutherian mammalian evolution which culminated in the evolution of man. His exacting mode of internal reproduction has been in existence for 60 million years, handed down and modified slightly from generation to generation.

There is little reason to believe that if life had evolved or is evolving on any other planet the prolonged step by step process would be much different from that on earth.

All of the events that have occurred in life on earth are ingrained characteristics of living protoplasm given opportunity to unfold. If other planets ever developed life they would have the potential of evolution quite similar to what came about on earth. However, each step would depend upon the simultaneous appearance of an advantageous ecological environment.

The final steps in animal evolution was in the eutherian mammals with blastocyst decidual type of burial implantation. But even this advanced and efficient system did not guarantee that all such mammals would eventuate into *Homo sapiens*. This may have related to opportunity. Man has had many lucky breaks in his 60 million years of evolution from the phyllostomid bats. His early ancestors lived in trees where they fortunately all had important prehensile thumbs. Fortunately, these ancestors were forced out of the rain forest at exactly the right time before they began to lose the prehensile thumb. On the ground they again were fortunate in having their fur coats infested with avaricious invertebrate arthropods which compelled the host to further develop the finer muscular abilities of the thumb and further develop microscopic vision in their eyes. These features improved their brains enough for them to be able to comprehend and use simple tools. Once this has been achieved the rest of the road to civilization was relatively easy. Each tool led to another more complex forcing the brain to keep up in its comprehension. Finally this arrived to such a development that new tools could be mentally invented in some individual brain. Along with this came new social relationships including private property. The latter compelled enumeration and numbers to identify objects and led to symbols to identify concepts. Thus a written language was born. The interdependence of the sexes evolved the family.

Amoroso, E. C.: Comparative anatomy of the placenta. Ann. N. Y. Acad. Sci. 75: 855-872, 1959

Amoroso, E. C.: Marshall's Physiology of Reproduction, 1960.

Anderson, J. W. and Wimsatt, W. A.: Placentation and fetal membranes of the Central American noctilionid bat (Noctilio labialis minor). Am. J. Anat. 112: 181-201, 1963.

Barghoorn, E. S. and Tyler, S. A.: Microorganisms from the Gunflint Chert. Science, 147: 563-577, 1965.

Barghoorn, E. S. and Schopf, J. W.: Microorganisms from the late Precambrian of Central Australia. Science, 150: 337-339, 1965.

Barghoorn, E. S. and Schopf, J. W.: Microorganisms Three Billion Years Old from the Precambrian of South Africa. Science, 152: 758-763, 1966.

Boyd, M. M.: The oviduct, foetal membranes and placentation of Hoplolactylus maculatus (Gray). Proc. Zool, Soc., Series A., 112: 65-104, 1942.

Budker, Paul: The Life of Sharks. Columbia University Press. New York, 1971.

Clark, W. E. LeGros: The antecedents of man. Quadrangle Books, Chicago, 1960.

Clark, W. E. LeGros: History of the primates. The University of Chicago Press, 1963.

Colbert, E. H.: Evolution of the Vertebrates, John Wiley & Sons, Inc., New York, London, Sydney, Toronto, 1969.

Eckstein, P. and Zuckerman, S.: Marshall's Physiology of Reproduction, 1960.

Encyclopedia Americana: Americana Corp., New York, Chicago, Washington, D. C., 1961.

Encyclopedia, Britannica: Encyclopedia Britannica, Inc., Chicago, London, Toronto, 1972.

Encyclopedia of the Animal World: Elsevier International Projects Ltd., London, 1972.

Flynn, T. T.: The phylogenetic significance of the marsupial allantoplacenta. Proc. Linn, Soc. N. S. Wales. 47: 541-544, 1922.

Flynn, T. T.: The yolk-sac and allantoic placenta in Perameles. Quart J. Micro. Sci. 67: 123-182, 1923.

Flynn, T. T.: The uterine cycle of pregnancy and pseudo-pregnancy as it is in the diprotodont marsupial Bettongia cuniculus. Proc. Linn. Soc. N. S. Wales 55: 506-531, 1930.

Gerard, P.: Contribution a l'etude de la placentation chez les lemuriens a propos l'une anomalie de la placentation chez Galago demidoffi (Fisch). Arch. D'anat. Microsc. 25: 56-68, 1929.

Gerard, P.: Etudes sur l'ovogenese et l'ontogenese chez les lemuriens du genre Galago. Arch. de Biol. 43: 93-151, 1932.

Goin, C. J.: Amphibians. Pioneers of Terrestrial Breeding Habits. Ann. Rep. Smithsonian Institution, U.S. Government Printing Office, pp 427-445, 1959.

Goodall (van Lawick-Goodall), J.: My friends, the Wild Chimpanzees. Nat. Geographic Soc. Washington, D.C., 1967.

Gopalakrishna, A.: Studies in the Embryology of Microchiroptera. Part I, Proc. Ind. Acad. Sci. 26: 219-232, 1947. Part II, Ibid. 27: 137-151, 1948. Part III, Ibid. 39: 17-46, 1949a. Part IV, Ibid. 30: 226-242, 1949b. Part V, Ibid. 31: 235-251, 1950a. Part VI, Proc. Nat. Inst. Sci. India, 16: 93-98, 1950.

Grosser, O.: Human and comparative placentation, including the early stages of human development. Lancet 1: 999-1001, 1933. Lancet 1: 1053-1058, 1933.

Haeckel, Ernst: The Last Link. Adam and Charles Black, London, 1899.

Hamlett, G. W. D.: Notes on the embryology of a Phyllostomid bat (Glossophaga soricina soricina) Am. J. Anat., 56: 327-349, 1935.

Hamlett, G. W. D.: Delayed implantation and discontinuous development in the mammals. Quart. Rev. Biol. 10: 432-447, 1935a.

Hartman, C. G.: Studies in the development of the opossum Didelphys virginiana L. J. Morph. 27: 1-83, 1916.

Hartman, C. G.: Studies in the development of the opossum Didelphys virginiana L. J. Morph. 32: 1-142, 1919.

Hartman, C. G.: How large is the mammalian egg? A review. Quart. Rev. Biol. 4: 373-388, 1929.

Hartman, C. G.: Possums. University of Texas Press, Austin, 1952.

Hecht, M. K.: Amphibians. Encycl. Brit., 1972.

Herald, E. S.: Living Fishes of the World. Doubleday and Company, Inc. Garden City, N.Y., 1962.

Hertig, A. T.: Angiogenesis in the early human chorion and in the primary placenta of the macaque monkey. Contr. Embryol. Carneg. Instn., 25, 37, 1935.

Hertig, A. T., and Rock, J.: Two human ova of the pre-villous stage, having a developmental age of about seven and nine days respectively. Contrib. Embryol., 31: 65-84, 1945.

Heuser, C. H.: A study of the implantation of the ovum of the pig from the stage of the bilaminar blastocyst to the completion of the fetal membranes. Contrib. Embryol. 19 (No. 106): 229-244, 1927.

Heuser, C. H. and G. B. Wislocki: Early development of the sloth (Bradypus griseus) and its similarity to that of man. Carnegie Inst. Wash. Pub. No. 459, Contrib. Embryol, No. 144, vol. 25: pp 1-13, 1935.

Heuser, C. H. and Streeter, G. L.: Development of the macaque embryo. Contrib. Embryol. 29 (181): 15-58, 1941.

Hill, J. P.: The placentation of Perameles. Quart J. Micro. Sci. 40: 385-446, 1897-98.

Hill, J. P.: The developmental history of the Primates. Phil. Roy. Soc. London, B, 221: 45-178, 1932.

Hill, J. P.: The macroscopic features of the placentation of the water-shrew (Potamogale velox). Bio-morphosis, 1: 331-332, 1938.

Hoffman, L. H.: Placentation in the Garter Snake, Thamnophis sirtalis. J. Morph. 131: 57-88, 1970.

Houston, M. L.: The villous period of placentogenesis in the baboon (Papio sp.), Am. J. Anat. 126: 1-15, 1969.

Houston, M. L.: The development of the baboon (Papio sp.) placenta during the fetal period of gestation. Am. J. Anat. 126: 17-29, 1969.

Jones, F. Wood: The genitalia of Cheiroptera. J. Anat. 51: 36-60, 1917.

Jones, F. Wood: Some curiosities of mammalian reproduction. J. Obst. Gynaec. Brit. Emp. (part 1) 51: 416-437, (part 2) 51: 553-564, 1944. (part 3) 52: 55-70, 1945.

Lee, T. G.: Notes on the early development of rodents. Am. J. Anat. 2: X-XI, 1903.

Mahadevan, G.: Preliminary observations on the structure of the uterus and the placenta of a few Indian plasmobranchs. Proc. Ind. Acad. Sci. B, 11: 1-209, 1940.

Matthews, L. Harrison: Notes on the Genitalia and Reproduction of some African Bats. Proc. Zool. Soc. London 3: 289-346 plus plates, 1941-44.

McCrady, Edward, Jr.: The Embryology of the Opossum. The Wistar Institute of Anatomy and Biology. Philadelphia, 1938.

Metten, H.: Studies on the reproduction of the Dog-Fish. Phil. Trans. Roy. Soc. London series B, 230: 217-238, 1939.

Moghe, M. A.: Development and placentation of the Indian fruit bat, Pteropus giganteus giganteus (Brunnich). Proc. Zool. Soc. London, 121: 703-721, 1951.

Mossman, H. W.: Comparative morphogenesis of the fetal membranes and accessory uterine structures. Contrib. Embryol. Carnegie Institution of Washington 26: 128-246, 1937.

Mossman, H. W.: The epithelio-chorial placenta of American mole, Scalopus aquaticus. Proc Zoological Soc. B, 109: 373-375, 1939.

Needham, J.: Biochemistry and Morphogenesis. University Press, Cambrilge, 1950.

Newman, H. H. and Patterson, J. T.: The development of the nine-banded armadillo from the primitive streak stage to birth. J. Morph. 21: 359-424, 1910.

Newman, H. H., Freeman, F. N. and Holzinger, K. J.: Twins, a study of Heredity and Environment. Univ. of Chicago Press, 1937.

Nitecki, M. H.: Windows to the Precambrian: The beginning of life The University of Chicago Magazine 65: (No. 6) 17-24, 1973.

Noback, C. R.: Placentation and angiogenesis in the amnion of a baboon (Papio papio). Anat. Rec. 94: 553-567, 1946.

Noble, G. K.: The Biology of the Amphibia. Dover Publications, Inc., New York, 1954.

O'Rahilly, R.: Development stages in Human Embryos. Embryos of the first three weeks (Stages 1 to 9). Carnegie Institution of Washington. Pub. 631, 1973.

Parkes, A. S.: Marshall's Physiology of Reproduction. Longmans, Green and Co., London, New York, Toronto, 1960.

Patterson, J. T.: Polyembryonic development in Tatusia novemcinctus. (armadillo). J. Morph. 21: 359-423, 1910. Also, J. Morph. 24: 559-634, 1913.

Robin, H. A.: Recherches anatomiques sur les mammiferes de l'erdre des chiropteres. Ann. des Sci. Nat. 6 me. Serie, Zool., T. 12, pp 1-180, 1881.

Romer, A. S.: Origin of the Amniote Egg. Scient. Month. 35: 57-63, 1957.

Romer, A. S.: Vertebrate Paleontology. Univ. Chicago Press. Chicago, London, 1966.

Rose, E. P. F.: Echinoderms. Encyclopedia of the Animal World 7: 621-629, 1972. Elsivier Internat. Projects, London, 1972.

Schmalhausen, I. I.: The Origin of Terrestrial Vertebrates. Academic Press. New York and London, 1968.

Schopf, J. W.: Evolutionary significance of the Bitter Springs microflora. Proc. XXIV Internat. Geol. Congress Sect I. Precambrian Geology, Montreal: 68-77, 1972.

Schumann, E. A.: Extrauterine Pregnancy, Gynecological and Obstetrical Monographs. D. Appleton & Co. 7: 1-207, 1931.

Scrimshaw, N. S.: Embryonic growth in the viviparous Poeciliid Heterandria formosa. Biol. Bul. 87: 37-51, 1944.

Scrivastava, S. C.: Placentation in the Mouse-tailed Bat, Rhinopoma kinneari, (Chiroptera). Proc. Zool. Soc. Bengal 5: 105-130, 1952.

Simpson, G. G.: The First Mammals. Quart. Rev. Biol. 10: 154-180, 1935.

Simpson, G. G.: The Beginning of the Age of Mammals. Biol. Rev. 12: 1-47, 1937.

Simpson, G. G.: The principles of classification and a classification of mammals. Bull. Amer. Mus. Nat. Hist. 85: 1-350, 1945.

Smith, H. W.: From Fish to Philosopher. Doubleday & Company, Inc. Garlen City, N.Y., 1961.

Snodgrass, R. E.: Evolution of the annelida onychophora and arthropoda. Smithsonian Misc. Coll. 97: (No. 6) 1-159, 1938.

Springer, S.: Oviphagus embryos of Sand Shark, Carcharias taurus. Copeia: 153-7, 1948.

Stephens, R. J.: Histology and histochemistry of the placenta and fetal membranes in the bat. Tadarida brasiliensis cynocephala. Am. J. Anat. 111: 259-275, 1962.

Streeter, G. L.: Developmental horizons in Human Embryos. Age groups XI, 13 to 20 somites. Age groups XII, 21 to 29 somites. Carnegie Inst. Wash. Contrib. to Embryol. 30: 211-245, 1942.

Streeter, G. L.: Developmental horizons in Human Embryos. Age groups XIII and XIV. Contrib. Embryol. 31: 27-63, 1945.

Streeter, G. L.: Developmental horizons in Human Embryos. Age groups XV, XVI, XVII and XVIII. Carnegie Inst. Wash. Contrib. to Embryol. 32: 133-203, 1948.

Streeter, G. L.: Developmental horizons in Human Embryos (fourth issue). A review of the histogensis of cartilage and bone. Carnegie Inst. Wash. Contrib. to Embryol. 33: 151-186, 1949.

Storer, T. I. and Usinger, R. L.: General Zoology. McGraw-Hill Book Co., New York, Toronto, Londn, 1957.

TeWinkel, L. E.: Notes on the Smooth Dogfish, Mustelus canis, during the first three months of gestation. J. Exp. Zool. 122: 123-37, 1963.

Torpin, R.: The Human Placenta: Its Shape, Form, Origin and Development. Charles C. Thomas, Springfield, Ill., 1969.

Torpin, R.: Placentation and Mammalian Phylogeny. Obstet. Gynec. 37: 942-948, 1971.

Turner, C. L.: The unique nutritional organs in the embryos of the top minnows of the Mexican Plateau. Science 77: 93-94, 1933.

Turner, C. L.: Viviparity superimposed upon ovo-viviparity in the Goodeidae, a family of the Cyprinodont Teleost fishes of the Mexican Plateau. J. Morph. 55: 207-251, 1933-34.

Turner, C. L.: Adaptations for viviparity in embryos and ovary of Anableps anableps. J. Morph. 62: 323-349, 1938.

Turner, C. L.: Adaptations for viviparity in Jenynsiid fishes. J. Morph. 67: 291-297, 1940.

Turner, C. L.: Pericardial sac, trophotaeniate, and alimentary tract in embryos of Goodeid fishes. J. Morph. 67-89, 1940.

Turner, C. L.: Pseudoamnion, pseudochorion, and follicular pseudoplacenta in Poeciliid fishes. J. Morph. 67: 59-89, 1940.

Turner, C. L.: Follicular pseudoplacenta and gut modifications in Anablepid fishes. J. Morph. 67: 91-105, 1940.

Turner, Wm.: An account of the Great Finner Whale (Balaenoptera sibbaldii) stranded at Longniddry. Pt. I: The soft parts. Trans. Roy. Soc. Edin., vol. 25, pp. 197-251, 1870.

Turner, W.: Lectures on the comparative anatomy of the placenta. Edinburgh, 1876.

Waters, A. J.: Personal communication.

Walker, E. P.: Mammals of the World. Three volumes. The Johns Hopkins Press, Baltimore, 1968.

Weekes, H. Claire: A note on reproductive phenomena in some lizards. Proc. Linn. Soc. N.S. Wales, vol 52, pp. 25-32, 1927.

Weekes, H. C.: On placentation in reptiles. Proc. Linn. Soc. N.S. Wales, vol. 54, pp. 34-60, 1929.

Weekes, H. C.: On placentation in reptiles: II. Proc. Linn. Soc. N.S. Wales, vol. 55, pp. 550-576, 1930.

Wilson, J. T.: Continents Adrift. Readings from Scientific American. W. H. Freeman and Company. San Francisco, 1972.

Wimsatt, W. A.: The placentation of a vespertilioned bat, Myotis lucifugus lucifugus. Am. J. Anat. 77: 1-51, 1945.

Wimsatt, W. A.: A reinterpretation of the structure of the placental barrier in Chiroptera. Anat. Rec. 117, 574, 1953.

Wimsatt, W. A.: The fetal membranes and placentation of the tropical American vampire bat Desmodus rotundus murinus. Acta. Anat. 21: 285-341, 1954.

Wimsatt, W. A., and A. Copalakrishna: Occurrence of a placental hematoma in the primitive sheath-tailed bats (Emballonuridae), with observations on its structure, development and histochemistry. Am. J. Anat., 103: 35-68, 1958.

Wislocki, G. B.: Experimental studies on fetal absorption. I. The vitally stained fetus. II. Behavior of the fetal membranes and placenta of the cat toward colloidal dyes injected into maternal blood-stream. Cont. Embryol. Carneg. Instn. 11, 45-60, 1920.

Wislocki, G. B.: On the placentation of the sloth (Bradypus griseus). Carnegie Inst. Wash. Pub. No. 361, Contrib. Embryol. No. 78, vol. 16, pp. 5-21, 1925.

Wislocki, G. B.: Further observations upon the placentation of the sloth (Bradypus griscus) Anat. Rec. 32, 45, 1926.

Wislocki, G. B.: On the placentation of the tridactyl sloth (Bradypus griseus) with a description of some characters of the fetus. Contrib. Embryol. 19: 209-228, 1927.

Wislocki, G. B.: Further observations upon the minute structure of the placentation of the sloth (B griseus). Anat. Rec. 40: 385-395, 1928.

Wislocki, G. B.: On the placentation of the two-toed ant-eater (Cyclopes didactylus). Anat. Rec. 39: 69-79, 1928.

Wislocki, G. B.: An unusual placental form in the Hyracoidea. Carnegie Inst. Wash. Pub. No. 407, Contrib. Embryol. No. 122, 21: 83-95, 1930.

Wislocki, G. B.: Placentation in the marmoset (Oedipomidas geoffroyi) with remarks on twinning in monkeys. Anat. Rec. 52: 381-399, 1932.

Wislocki, G. B. and C. H. Heuser: The similarity of the early development of the sloth (Bradypus griseus) to that of man. Anat. Rec. Suppl. vol. 52: 43, 1932.

Wislocki, G. B.: The placentation of the manatee (Trichechus latirostris). Mem. Mus. Comp. Zool., Harvard College, vol. 54, 159-178, 1935.

Wislocki, G. B. and Fawcett, D. W.: The placentation of the Jamaican bat (Artibeus jamaicensis parvipes). Anat. Rec. 81: 307-318, 1941.

INDEX

209

The Author:

Born, Oakdale, Nebraska, 1891
Graduate, Oakdale High School, 1909
Nebraska Wesleyan University, A.B. (French),
 1913
University of Chicago, S.B. (Anatomy),1915
Rush Medical College, M.D., 1917
Intern, Cook County Hospital
Lt., Med. Corps, U.S. Army, 1918-19
Following 7 years of rural medical practice;
Clinical Assistant, Ob. & Gyn., Rush Medical
College, 1931-36; Prof. & Chairman Dept. Ob. &
Gyn., Medical College of Georgia, 1936-58; Prof.
& Chairman, Dept. Ob. & Gyn., Shiraz Medical
School, Shiraz, Iran, 1958-60.
Student of the human placenta, 1931-1974
During retirement, five years were devoted to
review of the literature of embryological investi-
gation of the past 150 years

Author of

Obstetric Labor, 1948
Fetal Malformation due to Amnion Rupture,
Charles C. Thomas, 1968
The Human Placenta; its Shape, Form, Origin
and Development. Charles C. Thomas, 1969

Member of

American Medical Association
American College of Obstetrics and Gynecology
American Association of Anatomists
American Society of Zoologists
             Present Address:
          Richard Torpin, M.D.
          2618 Walton Way
          Augusta, Georgia 30904